RECIPES FOR HEALTHIER CHILDREN
A Mother's Guide

Recipes for Healthier Children

A Mother's Guide

Edith Redman

D.C. Heath Canada Ltd.
Toronto

Design & Illustration by Marcia Schrei

PAPERBOUND   ISBN   0-669-80648-X
CLOTHBOUND   ISBN   0-669-80663-3

Dedicated to
Sara and Suzanne, my daughters
and
Adrian, my husband
without whom none of this
would have occurred

Foreword

I am extremely impressed by this book. I have met the author briefly, but it is not her personality alone that produces the feeling I have for this book.

Edith Redman is a woman who, at 38 years of age, chose to "reverse" an international trend and go from career woman to mother. With this move, she brought a logic and determination to an "art" that has often been assessed as an "instinct."

In this era, we are assailed from every side by so called experts—especially in the kitchen. Experts usually lack one essential quality—feeling. Edith has feelings for her subject that come over loud and clear, unobstructed by the strictures of "writing for other experts" that are so often a barrier to communication.

Consider her statement:

"...a healthy newborn baby is the most perfect thing that anyone can hope to see, full of potential, health and happiness."

This is the key that has unlocked the book you hold now in your hands. Unfortunately, so many cookbooks get no further than being held, In this case, as a Mother—past, present or future—you are holding not a book but a life in your hands.

It is entirely possible that the contents of this book can have a dramatic effect upon your own life as well as your children's. People who care for other people in the daily business of cooking at home have a special aura about them. I believe they can be described as "good people."

Please read this book and take its feeling to heart so that you and yours may live in peace and happiness and may grow to be sane, sincere and strong participants in our troubled world.

Graham Kerr
Antigua, West Indies
1973

Acknowledgements

Many thanks to all the people who helped me with this book, especially my mother-in-law, Phyllis Hulbert, whose interest in good nutrition has always encouraged my husband and me; my friend, Stevie Ruys de Perez, a believer, who encouraged me when the going was rough, my editor, Jane Lind, who guided when it was needed, Rolf Zimmerman who has always been a source of encouragement, and all the people who care enough about their children's nutrition to read this book.

Table of Contents

Introduction

This book was born because of the interest in good nutrition I found I shared with many mothers, and it has been written out of my own experience as a mother. I do not claim to be a nutritionist, and this book is by no means a guide to feeding children with eating or medical problems. Good nutrition to me is just commonsense eating.

For our grandmothers there was no question of giving canned foods to infants, no instant this or that, no packaged cereals. Just mothers' milk, supplemented later by home-ground grains, home-maid breads, home-chopped fruits, vegetables and meats, the then "accepted" forms of baby foods.

Today many mothers, instead of enjoying their babies, worry about formulas and how soon the baby can have "solid" food. They worry about what to do if certain foods don't agree with their child and so set up problems for themselves before they even start. But happily, as we are becoming more conscious of ecology and our environment, many of us are beginning to discover a happy compromise between our grandmothers' day and the modern mothers' worries about nutrition. We are more interested in natural foods — foods that are grown without benefit of chemicals and marketed free of preservatives — foods that taste and look better. Many of us feel we need more time to spend with our children and in preparing their food so that they become happier and healthier. After all, a healthy newborn baby is the most perfect thing that anyone can hope to see, full of potential health and happiness.

Not many mothers want to be good doctors but all of us want to be good mothers. In the context of this book, this means mothers who have learned how to nourish a child, how to protect him from both excesses and deficiencies in his diet. In the past few years, I have had many friends and acquaintances ask me, "What are you giving your baby?" "How is it your babies look so healthy?" Some have told me I was lucky, but I suggest that it was not luck but rather good nourishing food and care that should get the credit. As a result I received many enquiries about recipes for childrens' meals and so began to look for a comprehensive cookbook for mothers interested in cooking with natural foods, and who realized that a better way of eating would make for a happier and healthier child. And isn't that what we all want for our children? I could not find a cookbook that satisfied me, so in this book I have gathered together recipes of my own and others that I think you will enjoy. Maybe you will end up using many of them for the adults in your family, too.

Your child's health and happiness is entirely dependent on you. The love we give our children in those early years, asking no return, brings its own reward. A family is a basic social unit and should supply a child with a worthwhile environment to grow and mature in. This sort of wealth springs from the parents' desire to contribute towards their child's upbringing in all senses of the word.

A mother plays a very large part in the family unit. It is she who will mold the child more than anyone, mentally and physically. Poor material conditions with plenty of genuine love provide a better background for a child than materialistic wealth and a shortage of affection. One of the most important duties a mother has is to see that her child is allowed to have a nourishing and healthful diet. This will be time consuming, and will take a conscious effort on her part.

Wherever possible I have used, and I suggest that you use, unrefined flours and foods. I have specified whole grains as opposed to "enriched" and refined products; honey, brown sugar, and molasses instead of white sugar; unhydrogenated vegetable oils instead of lards and hydrogenated vegetable shortenings; sea salt rather than iodized salt.

So cook, eat, and enjoy. I hope you will learn something new about food from this book and perhaps through it will discover some of the pleasures of cooking creatively and naturally.

Facts About Nutrition During Pregnancy

I had my first baby when I was 38. I was a career woman and had never as much as changed a diaper before. I knew which end was which but that was about the extent of my experience. I had to start from scratch, so I started to read. I read all I could find out about pregnancy, babies, and about looking after myself. I even found I was looking at daily astrology charts to see if anything of great portent might happen that day. It never did. But the important thing was that I *felt* it did. I wanted my baby and I felt great. This was a whole new important career for me and my husband.

I went to bed early, ate very well, did not get overtired, felt and looked tremendous. The only drastic thing that happened with my eating habits was that I could no longer drink and enjoy spirits. By this time I had read so much about how to and what not to do, that I found a lot of my thoughts about food were changing. It made a lot of sense to me that what I ate would ultimately affect me and my baby. After all, my body was working overtime and needed extra support. I was still working and therefore I needed all the energy and help I could get.

So I took my brewers' yeast and my food supplements regularly. And still I continued to feel super. With both my babies I was actually working on the last day before their birth and had to make my excuses to leave for the hospital. Friends said I was lucky. I say it was good management, from reading and taking heed. It all made such good sense. My body was working harder so I had to take more care of myself and give myself all the help I could.

During my pregnancy I began many new things. I started making my own bread, and am still doing so. I rediscovered the art of eating salads. Not the odd few limp leaves, but mouth watering assortments of fresh greens, nuts, and fruits. But enough about my own pregnancy, which to me, of course, was the only pregnancy in the world that had been like this.

One way to be sure you feel good when you are pregnant is to follow such a simple rule. DONT OVEREAT.

The majority of the pregnant women who pile on surplus weight do overeat. Overeating can be rationalized by ideas such as, "I feel hungry all the time," and "An expectant mother should have all the nourishment she can get". OR, "Well, I'm feeding two you know," and, "I have this special problem. I gain weight when I so much as look at a cookie", and so on *ad nauseum.* I think there is some sort of unspoken rule that because you are pregnant you deserve special things, and one of the special things you deserve is lots of food. Many times food is a substitute for the special attention you want. In reality, giving yourself more food than your body needs, is not treating yourself very specially but is actually hurting yourself.

There is a lot of truth in the saying, "You are what you eat". And at no time is this more true than now, when you are pregnant. Don't give in to the wish to nibble indiscriminately. Forget that luscious Danish and heavenly fried egg sandwich. And who really needs four coffees a day with cream and sugar? Such a lot is said about cravings for food during pregnancy. If you have a well-balanced diet you do not need peanut-butter-and-frogs'-legs sandwiches during the night. All that additional weight is hard to lose after the little one has arrived, and believe me, you will need all the energy you can muster to care for your baby!

My own rule of thumb was never to have any more to eat after I began to have that "full up" feeling. It's fatal, and in later months can be uncomfortable.

I think it is up to you to contribute something of your own to your diet. Don't just take for granted the chart the doctor thrusts into you hand. Find out what is meant by eating well. Find out what it will do for you. Doctors do hand out food charts to hundreds of women, but each person requires her own balance of vitamins and calories. We hear so much of Vitamin C and the B complex and polyunsaturated fatty acids, that it may help you to see this basic vitamin description which proved very helpful to me.

Vitamin Values

Vitamin A (Retinol or Carotene)
Best food sources: Fish liver oil, carrots, beef liver, parsley, kale, egg yolk, dried apricots, Swiss and cheddar cheeses, yellow fruits and vegetables, and fish. Insoluble in water so little is lost in cooking, unless very high temperatures are used. Store oils in fridge as they turn rancid quickly. You should keep only a small supply on hand.

Vitamin B-1 (Thiamin)
Best food sources: Brewers' yeast, wheat germ, soya bean flour, dried beans, whole wheat, powdered non instant skim milk, soya bean sprouts, egg yolks, liver, rice polishings, also pork, nuts, leafy vegetables, organ meats, oatmeal and lean meats. Soluble in water, so never discard cooking water.

Vitamin B-2 (Riboflavin)
Best food sources: Brewers' yeast, milk, liver, kidney, dried whey, wheat germ, turnip greens, cheddar cheese, powdered skim milk, egg yolks, soya bean flour, beet tops, lean meat, legumes. Exposure to light causes loss, so store away from light.

Niacin
Best food sources: Brewers' yeast, peanuts, liver, kidneys, veal, fish, wheat germ, leafy vegetables, canned salmon.

Vitamin B-6 (Pyridoxine)
Best food sources: Brewers' yeast, blackstrap molasses, brown rice, wheat bran, soya bean flour, kidneys, liver, dried non instant skim milk, cornmeal, barley, rye flour. Value is lost in exposure to light and long storage.

Vitamin B-12 (Cobalamin)
Best food sources: Liver, kidneys, muscle meats, milk, skim milk powder, whole milk powder, fillet of sole, Swiss cheese, eggs.

Other B Complex Vitamins

Choline
Best food sources: Brewers' yeast, liver, wheat germ, organ meats, egg yolk.

Folic Acid
Best food sources: Green leafy vegetables, dried legumes, asparagus, broccoli, nuts, whole wheat products.

Inositol
Best food sources: Cantaloupes, peanuts, raisins, beef heart.

Pantothenic Acid
Best food sources: Brewers' yeast, liver, kidney, heart, wheat germ, rice polishings, whole-grain breads and cereals, and green vegetables. Value is lost in heat.

   B Vitamins are stored in the body, so some of these foods should be eaten daily, and especially when you are pregnant. The B vitamins are lost in the urine and it has been found that when one drinks coffee they are washed through the body even more quickly.

Vitamin C
Best Food Sources: Rose hips, acerola cherries, guavas, parsley, turnip greens, green and red peppers, watercress, strawberries, oranges, lemon, grapefruits, tomatoes, soya bean sprouts, also liver, shellfish, fish, and most fresh vegetables and fresh fruits have a substantial amount. This vitamin is water

soluble, so wash and dry foods quickly, and cook in least possible time. Exposure to air is also destructive, so eat vitamin C-rich foods as raw as possible. Keep vegetables and fruits refrigerated. Essential for the pregnant woman and growing child, as it builds up resistance to infection and is important for the structure of bones, muscles, and sound teeth.

Vitamin D
Important for good bone structure, and necessary for the absorption of calcium and phosphorus.
    Best food sources: Fish liver oils, sardines, egg yolks, butter, liver, sunshine.

Vitamin E (Tocopherols)
Medical investigations are still undetermined as to all of the various uses of this vitamin. But it is known to be necessary in building body cells, so it is essential to the pregnant woman's diet.
    Best food sources: Oils of all grains, nuts, seeds, (wheat germ oil, soya bean oil, corn oil, peanut oil), wheat germ, dried navy beans, brown rice, green peas. Lengthy storage, freezing, and processing methods destroy this vitamin. Buy organically grown, fresh, unprocessed whole grains and seeds for maximum benefit.

Vitamin K-2 (Methyl — 1-41-Napthoquinone)
Important for the coagulation factor which causes blood to clot. Best food sources: Milk, unsaturated fatty acids, green leafy vegetables, alfalfa, egg yolks, liver, soyabean oil, cabbage, spinach. Heating and cooking and general preparation do not seem to affect this vitamin.

Minerals

Calcium: Important for good bone structure. Women who are suffering a lot from leg cramps can alleviate their discomfort by increasing their daily intake in tablet form. Best food sources: Bone meal powder, skim milk powder, whole milk powder, Swiss cheese, yoghurt, dried whey, blackstrap molasses, egg yolks, soya bean flour, turnip greens, dried figs, fresh milk, brewers' yeast powder. Calcium is constantly excreted so there should be a daily intake. A good source for pregnant mothers is 1 lb. of brewers' yeast powder mixed with ¼ cup powdered calcium lactate and used daily in the Tigers Milk drink.
Phosphorus;
Best food sources: Brewers' yeast, dried food yeast, wheat germ, skim milk powder, sardines, rye flour, liver; dried peas and beans, peanuts, English walnuts, pecans, bone meal, milk, cheese, meat, all unrefined foods.

Iron
Best food sources: Brewers' yeast, egg yolks, soya bean flour, blackstrap molasses, wheat germ, kidneys, liver, dried peas, beans, apricots; dried peaches, cashews, rye flour, parsley, raisins, prunes, whole grains. Deficiencies in this mineral will cause anemia. Nutritionists tell us that our system absorbs only half the iron we eat. The rest is eliminated. So to be sure that as a pregnant mother you are getting a complete supply, an iron supplement may be taken. Iron in foods is never toxic. Some supplements can be. Be sure you have an organic source that your body can readily assimilate.

Iodine
Best food sources: Dulse (sea weed), Irish moss, kelp, iodized salt, ocean fish and some seafoods.

Magnesium
Best food sources: Nuts and seeds; fruits and leafy vegetables if grown without the aid of chemical fertilizers.

Potassium
Best food sources: Meats, fish, dried navy beans, lima beans, split peas, dates, almonds, unrefined cereals and breads, green leafy vegetables.

At no other time are your nutritional requirements so high as when you are pregnant. The hard work of reproducing another human beging is a natural process of the body. But an adequate pre-natal diet is essential for the body to do its work. Learning to eat wisely and well will help you to enjoy your pregnancy more, and you, your baby and your husband will all benefit. And most important of all, enjoy your baby when it arrives. This is the most important time of your baby's life, and you are the one who starts him on his way. His beginnings will decide his future.

I had boundless energy all the time I was pregnant and I attribute a lot of it to my daily health drink or Tigers Milk as it is known. Do try it.

Mid Morning Health Drink or Tigers Milk

½ cup of your favourite fruit, such as banana, crushed pineapples, berries, frozen orange juice

2 tbsp. vegetable oil such as soya oil, or safflower

1 or 2 cups fresh skim milk

½ cup powdered milk

2 tbsp. brewers' yeast, gradually working up to ½ cup

½ tsp. vanilla (optional)

1 raw egg yolk

Blend in blender and add more milk if too thick.

Drink mid-morning and mid afternoon if you feel like it. Start by making half of the above quantity and gradually work up to the whole two cups.

Your Baby's First Foods

Presupposing that all babies are either ideally breastfed or on some sort of formula, the recipes in this section are additional supplements to the diet. When you want to start your child on solid food is up to you and your doctor. Many times a competition originates with mothers in the hospital when the woman in the next bed says proudly that her child is gaining x number of ounces per day. This competition continues through the babies' early months and years, the first mother feeding her baby the most solid food first. And so her baby gains so much more than Mrs. Smith's baby, and her baby has more teeth earlier than Mrs. Smith's baby, and walks, too. So what? Health and well being are what matter, and any sensible mother knows that her child differs from someone else's in more ways than one. My children were nursed completely for five months and then I gradually introduced more solid food, supplementing still with breastfeedings till they were one year old.

I believe that the most perfect food in the world for a baby is mothers' milk, especially the milk from a mother who cares about her nutrition and is in good shape. There are also many advantages to breastfeeding: the milk is more easily digested; it's always at the right temperature; it's always available. The nighttime feedings are easier and it is certainly an economical way to feed your baby. Besides all these practical advantages, breastfeeding provides a natural bond between you and your child which cannot be experienced in any other way.

When you are breastfeeding do remember to take it easy with spicy foods, wines, and strongly flavoured vegetables for the first seven weeks or so. Many a mother does not realise that whatever she eats reacts with the baby, sometimes quite violently.

When you give your baby his first taste of solid foods (be it cereal or pureed fruits) the texture will be so alien to his tastebuds that he may balk in the beginning. But usually a healthy baby from 3 months old gradually accepts whatever is given him, provided it is introduced in small enough quantities. An egg teaspoon or coffee demitasse spoon will easily be enough for his first try of solid food.

After your baby is used to solid food, you can begin to try out the many combinations of vegetables and fruit. He will soon let you know what he likes and what agrees with him, and you might be surprised at how little he turns down. So many of us do not give a child a fair chance at trying certain foods because of our own likes and dislikes. That approach lacks fairness.

I believe that preparing food at home with a blender for an infant is much better than buying prepared baby food. The foods you prepare yourself are fresher and therefore more nutritious. It takes less time than you imagine. And you might add up the cost of baby food and formula for six weeks to discover that you have probably saved enough money to invest in a blender. Blenders are an excellent investment, and if you have a juicer too, so much the better. If you have neither blender or juicer, don't despair. Use an ordinary strainer or a piece of cheesecloth or nylon.

I have found through trial and error that vegetable and fruit purees made and stored in the freezer in ice cube trays are very helpful. They are just the required amount for a first serving for baby and so easily warmed in a pan of hot water. An efficient method is to place an egg cup full of food in a pan of hot water and let stand for a few minutes.

The more care you take with your child's diet, the richer will be his and your reward. It isn't "luck" that some mothers have happy contented babies who seldom know about colic and who sleep peacefully through the night. So much depends on *what* you are feeding him. Mealtimes, even for an infant, should be a happy time of day. No scoldings. Preparing his food is more than a chore. It is a work of love building health for your child.

The recipes given in the following pages have been tried and tested on normal healthy babies and toddlers. Children with allergies and special diet problems will not always find them suitable.

Mineral-Rich Water

½ cup organically grown almonds with skin
¼ cup oat flakes
¼ cup organically grown raisins

1. Place in a quart jar and cover with pure water.

2. Soak for two days in the refrigerator.

3. Strain the liquid and keep cold in a covered jar.

This may be warmed to room temperature and offered to baby to drink from the tip of the spoon or in a bottle whenever necessary. It is rich in iron and other minerals. The soaked almonds and raisins may be added to the family cereal. When your baby is 5 to 6 months old, his supply of iron becomes depleted and you can even increase the available iron by adding 1 tablespoon of unsulphured molasses to the strained liquid.

Purees

Carrot Juice Delight

One washed unpeeled medium-size carrot.

Put the carrot through the juicer. (If you use a blender, strain it before feeding to baby.)

At first two or three spoonfuls will be enough, though it's easily digested. Combinations of carrot and apple are good. You might also try the following combinations:

apple, carrot, and lemon
celery, parsley, and carrot
beet, celery, and carrot
carrot, grape, and apple
carrot with orange juice

Carrot stains clothes, so rinse soiled clothes immediately in cold water.

Banana Magic

small ripe banana
egg teaspoon of wheat germ
yoghurt to mix
(See end of chapter on making your own yoghurt at home.)

Mash the banana and wheat germ and add enough yoghurt to make it the required consistency.

Yield: 2 servings.

Can be stored in screw-topped jar in refrigerator till next day.

Apple Pulp

1 apple with core and seed
  removed

Scrape the apple with tiny spoon and feed to baby. Also can be given with a little yoghurt. Good car-type food.

Lemon Peach

1 peeled ripe peach
1 teaspoon fresh lemon juice.

Mash peach and add lemon juice.

Yield: 2 servings.
Can be stored in fridge till next day.

Citrus Cup

1 medium size peeled orange
¼ peeled grapefruit
¼ peeled lemon
1 tbsp. honey or maple syrup

Put all fruit in blender and blend for 10 seconds. Delicious.

Crushed Grapes

½ lb. grapes (seedless)
½ cup yoghurt

1. Blend in blender.

2. Add yoghurt to required consistency.

A real favourite with the babies.

Apple Sauce Supreme

2 lbs. apples, peeled and cored
¼ cup water
¼ cup honey or maple syrup

1. Cut up apples into quarters.

2. Cook over low heat for 20 minutes. (Do not overcook.)

3. Add honey or syrup.

4. Cool.

Babies love this without sweetening. Surplus can be frozen in ice cube trays. Peaches, pears, apricots and cherries can all be treated in the same way.

Banana Avocado Smoothie.

1 fresh ripe banana (deep yellow with flecked skin)
½ pear
¼ avocado

1. Pour enough pineapple or apple juice into the blender to engage the blades.

2. Blend and serve.

Optional:
For the older child sprinkle wheat germ in the serving dish.

Vegetable Avocado Drink

¼ avocado
¼ cup yoghurt
1 tbsp. raw peas
1 tbsp. raw grated carrot

Blend.

Optional: Stir in ½ teaspoon of raw wheat germ.

Raisin Avocado Supper

¼ cup papaya (if you happen to live where they are readily procurable)
¼ avocado
¼ cup raisins or prunes
½ cup yoghurt

Blend and serve.

Note on avocados.

Although classed as a fruit, the avocado provides more energy and nutrients, pound for pound, than almost any other food. Its digestibility approaches that of raw milk. Many minerals, and vitamins A, B, C, D, E, and K are all contained in this fabulous fruit. A good quantity of high quality protein and a naturally unsaturated fat lie safe and protected within its unsprayed green covering. Avocados are bland enough to blend with other flavours but have a good delightful flavour of their own. Purchase the fruit when it is hard and green and place it in a warm dark place to ripen. The fruit is ripe when it yields to a gentle pressure between the palms of the hands.

Vegetables

The same rule applies for vegetables as for the very first solid foods in feeding your baby. A little at first and always one vegetable at a time. This is not the time to make a soup of six different vegetables and then wonder which one gave your baby an upset stomach.

I steam all my vegetables. I never peel them unless it is absolutely necessary. I wash and steam the vegetables in a minimum of water, always taking care to save the water because it contains valuable minerals and it can be used as a broth or simply to mix the vegetables. At first, avoid strong-tasting vegetables, or gas-forming vegetables. There will be time enough for those later.

Since such small quantities are needed at first, you can cook two or three vegetables at once and after blending, put in screw top jars. They will keep for two or three days in the refrigerator, or you can freeze them in ice cube trays and warm as needed.

Carrot Puree

½ cup chopped carrots
1 egg teaspoon of wheat germ
1 tsp. honey
yoghurt to mix (optional)

1. Wash and scrape.

2. Steam in a minimum of water for 20 minutes.

3. Mash or blend in blender and add wheat germ and honey. If preferred, blend wheat germ with carrot.
Yield: 3 or 4 servings

Use the above recipe with any vegetables that are not too strong. Potatoes, leeks, sweet potatoes, yams, green string beans, peas, spinach, ground artichokes, and beets. As the baby progresses to more foods, make combinations of the above for him.

I introduced salads to my children at an early age the following way. I steamed things like sweet bell peppers, lettuce, tomatoes, and fed them small quantities. And very soon I stopped cooking them and blended them raw. Here are a few suggested combinations.

Sara's Favourite Salad

1 tomato, skinned	1. Blend tomatoes, celery, pepper till smooth.
1 small rib of celery	
1 sweet bell pepper, red or green	
1 tbsp. vegetable oil	2. Add lettuce leaves.
1 tbsp. fresh lemon juice	
1 tbsp. brewers' yeast	3. Blend in oil, yeast, and juice.
5 Boston, romaine, iceberg or bibb lettuce leaves	
½ cup vegetable broth or tomato juice	

A great way to introduce salad to young palates. Surplus can be added to your own evening or lunch soup.

Carrots and Peppers

1 medium carrot washed and slightly scraped	Blend all ingredients to required consistency and serve at once.
1 medium size green or red sweet pepper	
2 tbsp. tomato, apple or orange juice	

Cucumber Cool

(Particularly good for babies in the heat of summer.)

1 small cucumber
1 small tomato
juice of one lemon
2 stems parsley
5 stems watercress

Blend all ingredients to fine consistency. Store surplus in screw-topped jars. Will last three servings.

Leek Potage

1 medium size potato
5 leaves of spinach
1 small leek
1 tbsp. non-instant powdered milk
½ cup water or broth
1 tbsp. wheat germ
½ egg teaspoon vegetable extract like Marmite

1. Steam potato and leek for 25 minutes. For the last 5 minutes add the spinach.

2. Blend in blender.

3. Add milk, wheat germ, and Marmite.

4. Serve at once. Freeze surplus in ice cube tray or eat it yourself for lunch.

Green Bean Mix

1 cup washed and tailed string beans
1 small leek
½ cup yoghurt
¼ cup ground almonds

1. Steam beans and leeks for 20 minutes.

2. Blend in blender with yoghurt and nuts and serve.

Peas and Lettuce

1 cup fresh shelled peas
6 small leaves of lettuce
1 small onion
1 tbsp. wholewheat flour
1 tbsp. non-instant powdered
  milk
½ cup vegetable broth or water

1. Steam peas and onion for 30 minutes in water and then add lettuce leaves for 2 minutes.

2. Blend in blender and add rest of ingredients.

3. Serve at once and freeze surplus.

Green Limas

½ avocado
1 cup fresh limas or
½ package frozen limas
1 tbsp. broth or juice

Blend until smooth. If too thick add a little yoghurt. If using frozen limas do not refreeze. *Yield: 4 servings.*

Parsnip Lunch

½ cup parsnips washed and cut
  into small pieces
¼ cup carrot washed and sliced
¼ avocado or ¼ cup yoghurt
1 teaspoon almond butter
  (see butters)
¼ tsp. brewers' yeast

1. Place vegetables in a blender and blend until smooth.

2. Add almond butter and seasonings.

3. Run again in blender.
Yield: 2 servings.

A word about additions to your vegetables. By adding non-instant powdered milk to your vegetables, you are putting in extra nutrition and also creating a cream soup for your baby. This can be done with practically any vegetables of your choice. I have not mentioned seasoning at all, beyond vegetable extract, as I don't believe Baby needs it. But if you feel you must use salt, I think its best to use sea salt, and in small quantities. Brewers' yeast can be added to most soups as it adds protein and iron, and is not unpalatable in this form.

Cereals

Apart from the juice, purees, and vegetables, there are the all-important cereals. We tend to think in terms of the packaged baby cereals, but for mothers who want to try something more nutritious and adventurous, try making your own baby cereal. Of course I don't mean giving your baby Crunchy Granola, although I am sure that if this were ground down fine enough it would be acceptable.

I have had great success with making my own baby Muesli. This is a Swiss recipe discovered by a Dr. Bircher Benner, who is a world famous name in nutrition and healing. It is now used by countless mothers with their own added combinations. It can be bought as a baby cereal but is imported from Switzerland and is quite expensive. So with the aid of my blender I tried making my own. A word of caution. Do not introduce all the ingredients at once.

I started with one ingredient, and in one week worked up to all of them. My babies had their first cereal at 6 months, but do what is best for you. The great thing about Muesli is that it contains nuts, which are pure protein, and an important factor in building bodies. I have had a few mothers say to me, "How could you try nuts on a tiny baby's stomach?." If you grind nuts fine enough the child has no difficulty digesting them. I found it more economical when I had introduced all the ingredients of Muesli to make quite a large quantity and store it in airtight jars in the refrigerator.

For the older child I have included a more advanced recipe in the next chapter. But the basic ingredients always remain the same. This is a complete food and is enjoyed by children and parents alike. This amount is sufficient for a baby for a few weeks, starting with one teaspoonful and graduating to four. Mix it with yoghurt, if preferred, or let it stand overnight in milk. Start by giving only the ground oats and gradually introduce the other ingredients.

Muesli

1 cup rolled oats
1 cup millet flakes
½ cup raw wheat germ
1 cup almonds, cashews, or
filberts (add a little soya flour
to nuts when grinding to keep
blades clear)

1. Put each ingredient through the fine grind on your blender, or if you have a food mill, do it in that. Grind as fine as you can.

2. Mix all ingredients in a large bowl and store in airtight jars. Fruit can be added when you serve it, starting with mashed banana or grated apple. The traditional way of serving it is with apples and raisins. In this case, you would blend the raisins first.

Eggs

Eggs are rich in iron and full of protein, so they are an invaluable source of good nutrition. I did not give my children any egg till they were 6 or 7 months old, and then only the yolk. For me the best way to introduce eggs was very lightly boiled and only a little at first, because eggs, above all other foods are apt to give babies a reaction. I never had much luck with feeding my children scrambled eggs till they were almost a year old. And as the babies grew older, I found their favourite way of having an egg was boiled 4 minutes, and served with "soldiers" of toast. Of course, as time went on I cooked them in other forms — poached, added to soups, etc. I always try to buy fertilized eggs, and if possible brown ones — the brown foible being entirely mine. They look better. "Friendly eggs," Sara calls them. "Brown eggs are friendly, aren't they?" And I am inclined to agree with her.

A Word about Yoghurt

By now you will have noticed I mention yoghurt quite a lot and recommend it to be introduced early and used often. Yoghurt is older than time, and if you want to believe that it has in it the secret of eternal youth, good for you. But what is more important is the actual facts about its nutritional properties. Probably that is where the myth arose that it gives perpetual youth. Yoghurt can easily be made at home, although there are a few good brands of plain yoghurt on the market now. Try making your own for you will be delighted with your success. I do not recommend for children the gooey so called fruit yoghurts which are in the supermarkets. Look at the ingredients. They contain so many things other than the basic milk needed to make yoghurt that they are actually another product altogether.

The protein in yoghurt is partially predigested by the bacteria that forms in it as it is being made. This is one of the reasons it is so easily assimilated into the body, and this is the reason it is used for invalids and babies. The type of necessary bacteria that is in yoghurt thrives in the intestines and breaks down the milk into lactic acid. All the bugs and bacteria that can cause gas and putrefaction in your stomach cannot live in lactic acid. And what is more, yoghurt manufactures, while in your stomach, the complete group of B Vitamins.

Adele Davis, in her book, *Lets Have Healthy Children,* says it is like having your own Vitamin B factory in your stomach. She also tells us that when antibiotics have been administered it is even more important to take yoghurt daily because antibiotics kill any valuable bacteria needed in the stomach, along with the unwanted bacteria.

I remember when I brought home my firstborn she had in her mouth a few white patches which the doctor diagnosed as thrush. My doctor told me to give her (remember, she was only 7 days old) 2 egg teaspoons of yoghurt a day until it cleared up. In three days it was gone. Fantastic stuff. So don't be afraid to try mixing it with fruit and vegetables for your babies.

If you are unfamiliar with it yourself, try it. It is a most important food for nursing mothers. The flavour may seem a little sharp to you but add some frozen orange juice or fruit and nothing could be more delicious. Older children love it with honey or molasses. As your children grow you will find all sorts of ways they like it. Its great at the family table as a salad dressing.

The trick of making yoghurt is to always have a low steady temperature, not too high or too low. The ideal temperature is between 95° and 120°. If the whey separates into curds you "cooked" your yoghurt too long, and did not chill it quickly enough. But don't throw it out. Mix it up in the blender and serve it to baby with a little honey. And if the yoghurt does not thicken at all, which has happened to me, your culture was too old and your temperature not high enough. There is a very good electric yoghurt maker on the market now, available at most health stores, which is a boon if you make a lot of it. You can make yoghurt with cow's milk, goat's milk, soya milk, non-instant powdered milk, skim milk, and a very different flavoured yoghurt is to be had if you use evaporated milk.

Yoghurt

1 quart of any of the above
 kinds of milk
1 tbsp. plain yoghurt

1. Bring the milk to boiling point.

2. Cool to lukewarm.

3. Place the yoghurt in a glass or enamel bowl.

4. Pour the cooled milk over the yoghurt gently and mix gently but well.

5. Cover, and leave overnight in a warming cupboard, or on the stove beside a pilot light, or on the radiator.

6. When set to your liking, chill immediately, because if you don't you'll have a very sharply flavoured yoghurt similar to goats cheese.

Serve with fruit, maple syrup, honey, molasses.

Things To Chomp

When your baby begins to show signs of wanting to chomp on something other than his teddy bear or rattle, give him a baked crust of wholewheat bread. It should not be too large as he tends to soak it thoroughly and then trys to swallow it. Keep an eye on him when he first starts chewing crusts. For no, matter how hard the crust, he always manages to soak it more quickly than you expected and may gag on it. A stick of celery or carrot is good, too. Carrots are great to take with you when you take your baby visiting, and indeed so are most root vegetables, such as turnips or parsnips (not potatoes). And to make it extra good dip the end in honey.

Teething Cookies for Baby

2 tbsp. honey
1 tbsp. molasses
2 tbsp. vegetable oil
1 egg yolk beaten
½ cup soya flour
¼ cup wheat germ
½ cup wholewheat flour

1. Stir together the honey, molasses, oil, and egg yolk.

2. Add the mixed flours and enough wheat germ to make a stiff dough.

3. Since flours differ, if too thick add a spoonful of milk.

4. Roll to ¼-in. thickness, and cut into rectangles 1 by 1½ inches.

5. Place on an ungreased cookie sheet and bake at 350° till golden brown, about 15 to 20 minutes.

Makes about 4 dozen cookies.

Note: Do not use until your baby has been started on every food used in this recipe.

Rusks

Cut your wholewheat bread into 4"- by 2"-pieces, and dry slowly in the oven for one hour at 250°.

Bread, Cereals and the Like

Reams of words have been written about the "non value" of most of the commercial breads on the market today. No matter how much we are told that they have been "enriched" there is no getting away from the fact that our bread today is not as good as it was 30 years ago. Because of the shelf life and the storage factor, it has become imperative for the commercial baker to add preservatives. In the larger mills before the bread is baked, the "gold" of the grain (the wheat germ) is taken out and replaced with synthetic vitamins. Quite recently people have become aware that bread is rubbish most of the time, and happily the stores are slowly but surely, becoming stocked with more superior breads.

During some research I did recently, I was delighted to find that a million-dollar concern in Toronto had already started to market an honest to goodness healthier bread. No additives and only unrefined ingredients were used in the baking. The shelf life is not so long and they suggest you keep it in the refrigerator, but it is selling so well that other breads of the same ilk will be on the market soon. I asked the president of the firm why his firm was doing this and his answer was that there is a definite demand from the housewife for a better bread. A rare example of a business man who actually listens to the needs and wants of the housewife! In health food stores there has always been a better than average loaf of bread. If you have never been to a health store, I suggest you go visit one. It is not full of only "faddist" foods, and you will be surprised at the cross section of the public who do their shopping there. But even if you can buy good bread, forget about the mystique of breadmaking and forge ahead and try your own hand at it.

The best flour you can buy is stone ground wholewheat flour. Stone ground means that the flour has gone through a slower grinding process which separates the husk from the grain, and retains most of the nutrients and vitamins contained in a grain of wheat. The commercial milling process is quicker and hotter, and thereby destroys most of the natural goodness which is replaced in part by synthetic vitamins. There are large commercial mills in the United States that do stone grind their flour, but as yet in Canada there are only a few mills, so consequently you will pay a few more cents per pound for it. But think of it in terms of an investment for your family's health.

Stone ground wholewheat flour should be refrigerated (or even frozen) as there are no preservatives in it and its shelf life is not so long. I bake once a month, so I buy 25 lbs. at a time and usually use it up in one baking session.

Then I freeze most of the bread. As the children get older I find myself making larger quantities all the time; for as they bring more friends home, I find I give away more loaves. Children really do love hot home-made bread with butter and honey, if their palates have not been ruined with too many sweet cakes and cookies.

I have been asked what recipe I use. Well, I do of course use a basic recipe, which I have given here in this chapter, but every batch tends to be a little different because I am always adding or subtracting another ingredient or so. There are all sorts of grains to experiment with besides wholewheat. Soya, rye, millet, durum, buckwheat, oatmeal, rice, and if you can only buy the raw grains in your store, try grinding them yourself in your blender or food mill. Add a few cups of a different flour to your batch of bread to give it that extra fillip and make it exclusively yours. All sorts of tremendous combinations are discovered that way. And how nutritious they all are. Add blackstrap molasses instead of honey or use both. The quantity of water used always varies a little from batch to batch, depending on the type of flour used, and how you knead it that day.

My mother gave me one good piece of advice I have never forgotten in respect to breadmaking. Always have everything warmed. From the pans, flours, bowls, ingredients, to the room. Always, if you can, bake in a warm kitchen. When you work with yeast you are working with a living organism which requires tender loving care. And mix with love. You work that out for yourself. If your first batch of bread is not as good as it should be, don't despair, but try again.

I have also included nutritious bread mixes for biscuits, pancakes, and muffins, which are always good to have on hand for those hungry children.

Basic Wholewheat Bread

9 cups warm water
1 cup honey
½ cup vegetable oil (soya, safflower, etc.)
5 tbsp. granule yeast
20 cups (approx.) unsifted stone ground wholewheat flour
2 tbsp. salt

1. Allow yeast to soften in warm water, for about 5 minutes, along with the honey.

2. Then add approx. 6 cups of flour, the oil, and the salt, and mix well with a wooden spoon.

3. Add 6 more cups of flour and mix again.

4. Add enough of the remaining flour to make the dough easy to handle.

5. Turn out onto floured board. Add more flour if necessary.

6. Knead. Knead and knead. Knead until it feels good — not sticky, but warm and elastic. You may need a little more flour, or you may not have used quite all of the 20 cups. Every batch varies.

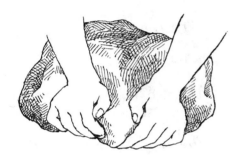

7. Set in an oiled earthenware bowl where it is warm, (on top of stove or radiator) and cover with a damp cloth. Let rise till the dough is double in bulk, usually one hour.

8. Punch down and turn dough over in bowl. Cover, and let stand one more hour in a warm place.

9. Turn the dough onto a board and divide dough into loaves. (From this recipe I get six 3-lb. loaves.)

10. Shape dough and put in greased pans in warm place for 20 minutes.

11. Bake in preheated oven at 350° for one hour, always remembering to allow a little space between each loaf in the oven (3 on upper shelf, 3 on lower). And there's your bread.

All sorts of your combinations can be added to the preceding recipe. It has never failed me. Addition of grains make the bread individually yours. When you require a crusty top, brush with beaten egg and milk just before putting into oven. Try rolling the top of the loaf in sesame seeds before you place it in the pan. If more chewy bread is desired, omit the oil. If crunchy bread is wanted, knead 1½ cups of soya grits or cracked wheat into the dough before forming the loaves. Try leftover potatoes or cereal in this basic recipe.

Bread Sticks for the Young Ones

(and grownups too)

4 cups wholewheat flour, stone-
   ground and unsifted
1 tbsp. dry yeast
1½ cups lukewarm water
1 tbsp. salt
1 tbsp. honey
1 egg, beaten

1. Dissolve honey and yeast in water.

2. Combine 3 cups flour and salt in bowl.

3. Stir in yeast mixture and enough of the remaining flour to make a fairly stiff dough.

4. Turn dough onto board and knead until it feels silky.

5. Divide into 48 pieces. Make a rope of each. (Children love to help with these. And the odd shape here and there contributes to it all.)

6. Brush with beaten egg and bake in a preheated oven at 425° for 12 to 15 minutes till browned.

Fun food which is nutritious too. Great for babies to chomp on and for lunch pails too.

The Most Crusty White Bread

10 cups unbleached white flour
 (obtainable at health stores)
1 tbsp. salt
2 tbsp. active dry yeast
1 cup lukewarm water (approx.)
½ cup safflower, soya or
 sunflower oil
1½ cups milk
2 eggs lightly beaten
4 tbsp. honey

1. Combine the flour and the salt.

2. Dissolve the honey and yeast in warm water, and add oil and milk. Mix well.

3. Combine the yeast mixture with flour and mix it well. (This is instead of kneading it, so mix it vigourously and well.)

4. Place in oiled bowl.

5. Cover and let rise till double in bulk, about 1 to 1½ hours.

6. Punch down, turn onto board, and pat or roll into ½-inch thickness.

7. Cut dough in four and roll like a jelly roll with tapered ends.

8. Place on oiled sheet and let rise for 20 minutes.

9. Slash tops with sharp knife.

10. Beat eggs and combine with a little milk and brush loaves thoroughly all over.

11. Set to rise for one hour in a warm place.

12. Preheat oven to 400° and bake for 15 minutes and then for 20 minutes at 350°.

Yield: four loaves, and watch them disappear.

A Nutritious and Versatile Quick Bread Mix

6 cups stone ground wholewheat
  flour
2 cups soya flour
½ tsp. salt
1 tbsp. double acting
  baking powder
1 cup non-instant powdered
  milk
2½ cups wheat germ
½ cup buckwheat grains

Mix all of the above ingredients and keep in an airtight jar in the refrigerator or cool place. You may add spices to this mixture as needed.

I have given a few examples of recipes that children love that can be used with this mix. Find out for yourself by adapting your favourite recipe with some of this mix: coffee cakes and muffins and pancakes.

Cinnamon Cake

1 cup seedless raisins
¾ cup boiling water
1 cup brown sugar
½ cup margarine
1 cup yoghurt or buttermilk
2 egg yolks
1¾ cups of our mix
1 tsp. cinnamon
2 stiffly beaten egg whites

1. Soak raisins in boiling water.

2. Meanwhile, cream together the sugar and margarine.

3. Add and beat well the yoghurt or buttermilk and egg yolks.

4. Sift in the dry ingredients.

5. Drain the raisins and add, being careful to coat the raisins well with flour.

6. Add to the other dry ingredients.

7. Blend well.

8. Fold in egg whites.

9. Pour into 8" greased pan and bake for 30 minutes at 350° When cooled it can be covered with uncooked icing.

Whole Wheat Banana Cake

1 cup stone ground wholewheat flour
½ cup nutritious mix
½ cup margarine
1 egg
¾ cup brown sugar
½ tsp. baking soda
1¼ cups mashed ripe bananas
¼ cup yoghurt or buttermilk

1. Cream margarine and sugar till creamy.

2. Beat in egg.

3. Sift together dry ingredients.

4. Combine the bananas and buttermilk or yoghurt, stirring just enough to mix.

5. Add dry ingredients and banana mixture alternately to creamed mixture, stirring just enough to combine.

6. Turn into oiled 5" x 9" pan.

7. Bake in a preheated oven at 350° for 50 to 60 minutes until done.

8. Cool in the pan 10 minutes, and then remove from pan and finish cooling on the rack.

Yield: one loaf. Great plain or with a nut butter.

Nutty Loaf for Family and Friends

3 cups of our mix
1 cup coarsely chopped nuts
1 egg
1 cup yoghurt
¾ cup brown sugar
½ cup soya oil

1. Combine nuts and the mix.

2. Add the other ingredients until well moistened.

3. Pour into a well-greased 1-lb. loaf tin and bake for one hour at 350°.

4. Turn out immediately onto rack to cool.

Note: Raisins can be substituted for nuts.

Sara's Favourite Banana and Oatmeal Muffins

1 cup oats
1 cup unbleached flour
1 tsp. sea salt
2 tbsp. brown sugar
2 eggs separated, at room
   temperature
½ cup milk, scalded
1/3 cup oil
1 tsp. lemon juice
1 small banana, mashed

1. Preheat oven to 375°.

2. Combine oats, flour, salt, and sugar in a bowl.

3. Lightly beat egg yolks and stir in the hot milk.

4. Beat in the oil, lemon juice and banana.

5. Sprinkle over yolk mixture and fold in gently.

6. Beat in the egg whites and fold into the batter.

7. Put into oiled muffin tins, 2/3 full.

8. Bake 30 minutes until golden brown.

9. Cool on a rack and keep them out of reach of the children or the muffins will never make the table.

Yield: About 20 muffins

Zurich Nut Bread

1 cup rye flour
2/3 cup unbleached white flour
2 tsp. baking powder
½ cup brown sugar
½ cup coarsely chopped walnuts
1-1/3 cups buttermilk

1. Mix flour and baking powder together.

2. Dust chopped nuts lightly with flour.

3. Add a small amount of warm water to sugar and stir till smooth.

4. Then stir in the buttermilk.

5. Quickly combine dry and liquid ingredients together. Add nuts and mix well.

6. Preheat oven to 300°.

7. Pour dough into well-greased bread tin and bake for 45 minutes.
Better still if served the following day.

Sunshine Muffins

3 eggs, separated
2 tbsp. soya, safflower or oil of
  your choice
2 tbsp. honey
½ cup unsweetened grated
  coconut
¼ cup wheatgerm
1 cup sunflower meal (make your
  own by grinding in your
  blender)
½ cup rice polishings
½ tsp. salt
1 cup raisins
½ cup apple juice

1. Preheat oven to 350°.

2. Beat egg yolks lightly and mix with other ingredients, except for egg whites.

3. Beat egg whites till stiff and dry.

4. Fold into the batter.

5. Fill oiled tins 2/3 full and bake 25 to 30 minutes.

Yield: 1 dozen muffins.

Do not worry about a leavening agent in these muffins. It is not needed. Muffins are chewy and quite heavy textured.

Muffins for Yoghurt Lovers

2 eggs, lightly beaten
1 cup plain yoghurt
2 tbsp. oil
¼ cup blackstrap molasses
1½ cup stone ground
  wholewheat flour
2 tbsp. soya flour
1 tsp. sea salt
½ cup raisins
¼ cup chopped nuts

1. Preheat the oven to 375°.

2. Combine the eggs and yoghurt.

3. Beat in the oil and molasses.

4. Sift together the flour, salt, and soya flour.

5. Add the egg mixture to the dry ingredients and stir well until moistened.

6. Stir in the raisins and nuts.

7. Fill oiled muffin tins 2/3 full.

8. Bake 20 minutes or until done.

Yield: 20 muffins

These muffins have no rising agent and are quite firm in texture. Good warm for breakfast.

Suzanne's Carroty Muffins

½ cup non-instant powdered
   milk or soya milk
2 tsp. baking powder
1 tsp. salt
½ tsp. allspice
½ tsp. cinnamon
2½ cups stone ground
   wholewheat flour
1 cup honey
1 cup safflower or other oil
4 eggs
1 cup grated apple unpeeled
1 cup grated carrot

1. Preheat oven to 400°.

2. In a large bowl combine the powdered soya or cow's milk, baking powder, salt, spices and flour.

3. Combine the honey, eggs and oil, and stir into dry ingredients.

4. Fold in the apple and carrot.

5. Spoon into oiled muffin tins.

6. Bake 15 to 20 minutes until done.

Yield: About 20 muffins

Cereals

Start savouring the texture and taste of a homemade cereal. The package you buy at the store may seem less expensive and certainly more convenient. But have you ever looked at how much weight you are really getting? Explore with your own combinations of the basic recipes I have listed here. Growing toddlers and older children need the good start of a nutritious and delicious breakfast cereal to help them keep up with all that energy.

Basic Breakfast Muesli for Toddlers and Older Children

All sorts of fruit can be added to the Muesli to make different combinations. It is better if soaked overnight. Three or four tablespoons of this is enough because it is very filling.

4 cups rolled oats (not instant)
1 cup nuts, almonds or filberts are good (break into smaller pieces for toddlers)
2 cups wheat germ
2 cups millet flakes
2 cups raisins
1 cup sesame seeds

1. Combine all ingredients in a bowl and store in .airtight jars. Use as desired.

2. Soak the required amount overnight with 1 tbsp. honey, 1 tbsp. fresh lemon juice, and cream, milk, or plain water.

The classic way to serve this Swiss cereal is with grated apples. But try it with your favourite fruits in season. Delicious. In the winter, if you prefer, put a little hot milk onto the cereal. But I find most children like it at room temperature.

Homemade Hot Cereal

1 lb. rye grains ground in blender
   till fine
1 lb. whole oats ground in
   blender till fine
1 lb. wheat germ
½ lb. bran ground in blender
½ lb. yellow corn meal
½ lb. brown sugar

1. Combine everything and mix well.

2. Store in screw-topped jars till ready for use.

3. When ready to cook: For two children, allow ½ cup to 1½ cups water, and a pinch of salt.

4. Cook by heating water to boiling.

5. Add cereal and beat vigorously.

6. Bring again to boil and let sit till the next morning.

7. Reheat slowly.

8. Serve with raisins, prunes and milk or cream.

This cereal takes a little more trouble but is ideal for children going off to school in those snappy winter mornings.

Try something a little different for tempting palates on winter mornings. Brown rice is a complete food in itself and has the advantage of tasting so much more delicious than ordinary rice. It takes a little longer to cook as it is still in its original form with the husk on.

Granola Type Cereal

(Easy to make breakfast cereal, snack, health food all in one.)

2 cups rolled oats, not the instant kind
½ cup safflower oil
¼ cup honey
¼ cup wheat germ
¼ cup sunflower meal (if not available grind your own seeds)
¼ cup sesame seeds
1 cup shredded unsweetened coconut
¼ cup raw nuts, almonds, filberts, etc.
¼ cup raisins

1. Combine all ingredients in large mixing bowl. (Add more nuts or raisins if you wish.)

2. Bake in shallow pan for 15 to 20 minutes at 350°.

3. Toast to golden brown.

4. Store in jars and use as needed. Serve with cream, milk and fresh fruit.

Nutritious Breakfast Cereal

2 pounds non-instant rolled oats
½ tsp. salt
1¼ cups soya oil
½ cup honey
¾ cup non-instant cows or soya milk
1 cup soya flour
1¾ cup wheat germ
1 pound finely chopped dates
1½ cups unsweetened coconut
1½ cups chopped dried apples
1 cup sunflower seeds
1½ cups raisins
1½ cups chopped nuts of your choice
1 cup pumpkin seeds (optional)

1. Preheat oven to 300°.

2. Place rolled oats in a large bowl.

3. Add salt and honey and mix well.

4. In another bowl combine all the remaining ingredients and mix well.

5. Stir in the oats mixture and mix well again.

6. Spread out enough of the

mixture to cover a large baking sheet.

7. Bake 15 minutes.

8. Transfer to bowl to cool.

9. Repeat with remaining oats mixture.

10. Store in tightly screwed jars in the refrigerator.

Serve with cream or milk. Great for munching.

Breakfast Rice with Prunes

For two children:

½ cup brown rice
2 cups milk, cow's or soya
½ cup cooked prunes
maple syrup or honey to taste.

1. Grind rice in blender till half the size.

2. Combine rice with milk in a saucepan.

3. Bring to a boil and simmer for about 20 minutes.

4. Serve with prunes and honey or maple syrup.

This can also be used as a dessert. It is unusual to serve rice for break-fast, but most of us forget that it is a cereal grain, and I found our children enjoyed the change.

This little collection of breads, cereals and the like would not be complete without a few of my favourite pancake recipes. I use them for lunches and fill them with all sorts of good things: fruits, chicken, and fish. And they always go down well.

Pancakes for Stuffing

For one child:

½ cup milk
¼ cup wholewheat flour
½ cup powdered milk
1 egg yolk
1 egg white

1. Combine milk and yolk of egg.

2. Stir in flour and milk powder.

3. Beat gently until mixed.

4. Fold in stiffly-beaten egg white.

5. Bake on moderately hot griddle pan, using a dab of oil. Use 2 tbsp. batter for each pancake. This makes four small ones.

Serve with lemon juice and a dab of butter and honey. Or fill with chopped fruit: banana and lemon; strawberries and lemon; peaches and lemon; or any berries in season.
Chopped chicken in cream sauce is a great winner. Flaked fish in cream sauce is not to be ignored. These pancakes can be made in larger quantities for a larger family and stored on a plate till next day when you heat them in a 300° oven.

Pancakes for Breakfast

For two children:

½ cup wholewheat flour
½ cup non-instant powdered
  milk
¼ tsp. salt
1 tsp. baking powder
¾ cup yoghurt
1 egg
1 tbsp. soya oil
¼ cup wheat germ

1. Sift dry ingredients except wheat germ into a bowl.

2. Add yoghurt, egg, oil, and wheat germ.

3. Stir till moistened. Do not overbeat.

4. Drop onto griddle and cook slowly.

5. Turn when tiny bubbles form and brown on other side.
Serve with dab of butter and maple syrup or honey. Good with fruit or scrambled eggs.

Barley Flour Pancakes

Let the children guess what the delectable and different flavour is

1 egg beaten
1/3 cup sour cream
1/3 cup buttermilk
1 cup barley flour
1½ tsp. baking powder
pinch of salt
1 tsp. raw sugar

1. Beat the egg, then add the cream and buttermilk.

2. Sift the flour and dry ingredients together and combine the two mixtures.

3. Let stand two minutes and fry on hot oiled pancake griddle.

4. Turn when brown and puffy. Turn once and finish.
Serve with butter and syrup or fresh fruit jam.

Makes 8 pancakes.

Vegetables, Fruits and Drinks

I have heard so many mothers say that they cannot get their children to eat vegetables. They say they have tried and the child has refused, except for his one or two favourites. Perhaps a lot of the problem is that they were introduced too late in their diet. Most children should have been introduced to various kinds of vegetables from 6 months on. There are valuable vitamins and minerals in vegetables which are needed for the growing body.

One has to remember that babies are individuals and as such are entitled to their likes and dislikes. If there are certain vegetables which they refuse time and time again, perhaps they genuinely dislike them, and that is fair enough. But perhaps Mother has not liked vegetables, and the child has sensed that he is being offered something that she doesn't really like.

I remember a woman who was helping with my first baby. She hated spinach with a passion. And she would always tell me that Sara did too. I watched her feed spinach to Sara one day, and sure enough her grimaces were enough to turn anyone off it for life. Some vegetables are strong tasting for the young palate and therefore will not be liked at first, but they are the exception. If you have been following the pattern for blending your vegetables as suggested in the previous pages then you will probably have no trouble.

I think there is no necessity to cook with salt for young children. There is usually enough salt in their food naturally. So many mothers add more salt because they think the food is too bland. But children like bland food, and in fact, at an early age, prefer it. There is certainly no nutritional advantage to adding more salt.

Vegetables should never be soaked in water. Wash just before using, and in many cases don't peel. Potatoes and carrots can be scraped, and in fact, often just washed. Then the children will become used to eating the skins. In many cases minerals and vitamins are so near the skin, especially in root vegetables, that if you cut off the peel or skin you are throwing away so much nourishment. And for goodness' sake, don't overcook.

For me, steaming is the most economical and most nutritious way of cooking vegetables. I recommend, too, cooking vegetables whole if possible. (And save the water from the steaming for gravies and broths.) If you are in a great hurry a good way to cook vegetables is to grate them and they will cook in a very few minutes. Babies and toddlers prefer their vegetables brightly coloured and crisp. Never cook green vegetables in soda. It does make them more green but it just happens to rob them of their vitamin content in doing so. If you don't overcook you will not have the problem of trying to keep them green.

As baby becomes older his vegetables can be more coarsely chopped. Here again, use your own discretion and check with your doctor if necessary.

Always try to serve the vegetables as fresh as you can. Remember that Vitamin C is lost when vegetables are exposed to the air too long. For this reason they need refrigerating. Garden fresh produce is preferable to frozen. But if the choice is between frozen and two-week-old produce then you will probably be better off with the frozen. We are lucky to have a plentiful supply of fresh produce all year round. And it is usually in more remote districts that only tinned vegetables have to be used continually.

After you have become aware of your childs needs, it will be very easy to cook small quantities. Do it in one pan. No harm in cooking them together as long as you remember that some vegetables take more cooking time than others. For example, potatoes, carrots, and turnips take longer than string beans, leeks and zucchini. And some leafy vegetables like spinach and lambs quarters take only a few minutes. Never throw out any vegetable water in which the vegetables were steamed or boiled. Use it for accompanying gravies or broths. There are so many nutrients in that water that it is sheer wanton waste to throw it out.

Boiling vegetables gently in milk is another delicious way of cooking them. And the milk need not be thrown out. It can be used in sauces or soups. When preparing cauliflower, you can neutralize the strong taste by cooking it in milk. I often do my vegetables in the oven if it is already on for something else. Cook them in a covered casserole with a few tablespoons of water. A delicious flavour is preserved this way. And, of course, there is the pressure cooker. But to make a pressure cooker worthwhile you do need to cook quite a quantity, so there are perhaps more economical ways of cooking for the children.

We have all experienced over-cooked vegetables which have not an ounce of taste left in them. Although babies' taste buds are not yet fully developed, they are present, and your children will feel more like eating vegetables that look crisp, mouthwatering and delicious.

Potatoes

Let's start with the good old potato. Always a favourite is the steamed-mashed-and-served-with-gravy kind. Baked potatoes are easy to do and fun to serve. They take approximately 45 minutes to do in a 400° oven. Baking them on the lowest shelf reduces the cooking time and makes the skins crisp. Remember to pierce them two or three times with a sharp knife to prevent exploding.

A good thing to know is that if you steam a potato with its jacket on you have a "baked" potato in half the time and you have not cooked the goodness completely out of it. Sometimes it is not economical to put the oven on for one potato and this is a first class method of substitution.

When cooked, potatoes can be stuffed with a variety of fillings which make them a complete meal. Don't dismiss the potato as too "starchy". The common old potato is rich in Vitamin C and many minerals. I like my children to eat the skin, and if it is first washed, rubbed with oil, and done to a crisp they enjoy it. I do not approve of cooking potatoes in foil paper. It may hasten the cooking time but you are left with a soggy skin, not the most appetizing way of urging your child to eat the "jacket" of the potato.

Here are a few suggestions for potato fillings.

Cheese Filling for Medium Size Baked Potato

2 ozs. grated medium or mild cheddar cheese
1 tbsp. yoghurt
1 small peeled and chopped tomato
suggestion of chopped leek or parsley or dill
1 tbsp. butter

1. Mix all ingredients together and pile into split baked potato.

2. Sprinkle with chopped parsley, leek, or dill.

Another good method is to scoop out the potato first and combine it with the cheese mixture and put it back in its skin. If desired, you can broil it under a hot grill for two minutes.

Vegetable Filling for a Medium Sized Baked Potato

1 small carrot, cooked and
  chopped
1 tsp. leek chopped
2 tbsp. yoghurt or sour cream
1 egg spoon of vegetable flavour-
  ing such as Marmite

Mix all ingredients, along with
the inside of the baked potato
and stuff back into the skin.
Serve with other vegetables
and/or meat dish.

Instead of the usual popular French-fried method, try this method for a
change. It's very quick, and does not use much oil.

Oven French Fries

2 medium size potatoes
3 tbsp. soya oil or oil of your
  choice

1. Peel and chip potatoes, as for
regular French fry.

2. Arrange in oven-proof
casserole and sprinkle oil all
over.

3. Churn around with a fork,
making sure all the potatoes are
oiled.

4. Put into preheated oven and
bake at 425° for 14 minutes. During that time turn once. If you
want them more browned, finish
them off under the grill for a few
minutes. If your children like the
flavour of onions, try adding a little chopped onion along with
the potatoes. They'll never be
turned down, I guarantee.

Scalloped Potatoes

2 medium size potatoes
1 small onion
½ cup yoghurt
¼ cup wheat germ
½ cup skim or homo milk
1 tbsp. butter
1 oz. grated cheese

1. Arranged layers of thinly-sliced potatoes and onions.

2. Mix milk, yoghurt, wheat germ and cheese.

3. Pour over potatoes and bake at 275° for one hour.

Tomato Jelly Mold

1 small green onion, chopped
1 cup skinned tomatoes
½ tsp. honey
1 tbsp. unflavoured gelatin
½ cup cold water or vegetable broth
1 cup blended tomato pulp
2 tbsp. fresh lemon juice
¼ cup finely diced celery

1. Boil the onion for 5 minutes in the cooked tomato pulp.

2. Add honey.

3. Soak the gelatin in water for 10 minutes.

4. Stir the hot pulp into the gelatin.

5. Add the cold tomato pulp, lemon juice, and chopped celery.

6. Place in small custard cups, or larger mold.

7. Chill until firm, approximately 2 hours.

Lightly tart flavour which children love. Appetizing for adults too.

Broiled Stuffed Tomatoes for Two

(known as "stuffened" in our house)

2 medium size tomatoes
2 ozs. grated mild cheddar
  cheese
¼ cup chopped parsley or leek
1 tbsp. lemon juice
1 tbsp. butter

1. Cut tomatoes in half.

2. Place on cooking sheet and broil for 20 minutes.

3. For young children, slip off skins after broiling. (Point of interest: Cooked tomato skins are the hardest things to digest.)

4. Sprinkle top with cheese, chopped parsley or leek, melted butter, and lemon juice.

Best Carrots and Beans

for two children

2 medium size carrots, washed
  and cut into coin shapes or
  sticks
½ lb. string beans, whole
1 tbsp. honey
1 tbsp. sesame seeds
½ cup vegetable water

1. Place carrots and whole trimmed beans in an oven-proof buttered casserole dish.

2. Pour honey and water over vegetables.

3. Sprinkle with sesame seeds. Preheat oven and cook for 45 minutes at 350°. Last 5 minutes take lid off casserole.

Carrots in Nutmeg Sauce

½ lb. carrots, washed and cut into coin pieces

Steam for 20 minutes or so and serve with nutmeg sauce.

Nutmeg Sauce

1 tbsp. wholewheat flour
1 tbsp. butter
½ cup milk
1 tbsp. lemon juice
pinch of freshly grated nutmeg.

1. Melt butter and add the flour, stirring constantly.

2. Add milk slowly over low heat, still stirring.

3. When thickened, and just before serving, add lemon juice and nutmeg.

4. Pour over carrots in a serving dish.

Turnips and Potatoes

for two

2 medium size potatoes, halved
1 small yellow turnip, peeled and cut into pieces
1 tbsp. butter

1. Cook potatoes and turnip for 30 minutes.

2. Mash together and add butter.
Delicious with plain or nut gravy.

Ratatouille for Children

for two

6 tiny eggplants peeled and sliced thinly
Sea salt (optional)
1 tbsp. soya oil
1 tiny leek or small onion sliced thinly
1 medium size zucchini, washed and sliced into coin shapes
1 small sweet bell pepper, seeded and sliced
2 tomatoes, skinned and sliced

1. Heat oil in skillet and saute leek or onion till tender.

2. Toss the zucchini with the flour and add to the skillet.

3. Cook over medium heat for 5 minutes.

4. Add all the other ingredients, cover and cook slowly till all the excess liquid has evaporated. Takes about 25 minutes. This can be transferred from the skillet to a covered casserole and cooked in the oven if preferred for 30 minutes at 350°. Serve hot or cold.

Yams or Sweet Potatoes

1 yam or sweet potato
2 tbsp. honey
2 tbsp. butter

1. Cook by steaming one medium size yam or sweet potato for 30 minutes until tender.

2. Cut in half.

3. Scoop out pulp and mix with 2 tbsp. honey and 2 tbsp. butter. Serve right away. Good with chicken.

Truly Turnip

for two

1 small yellow turnip (also called rutabagas), peeled and cubed
½ cup vegetable water or chicken broth
2 tbsp. honey
1 oz. grated mild cheddar cheese

1. Place turnip in buttered casserole.

2. Mix vegetable water with honey and pour over turnip.

3. Sprinkle cheese on top.

4. Cook it in medium oven at 325° for one hour.
My children make a meal of this served with nut mince poured over the turnip.

(Note:) Nut mince recipe on page 80

Cauliflower and Apples

for two

1 tiny cauliflower or two miniature cauliflowers, trimmed just to the flower. (The stalk is a little strong in taste for young palates.)
1 apple, peeled and chopped
1 tbsp. butter

1. Steam cauliflower and apples for 20 minutes.

2. Lightly chop cauliflower and apple together and serve with melted butter.

This combination of apple with the cauliflower seems to minimize the rather strong flavour of the flower, and is sweet to the taste.
Broccoli, kale, and spinach are delicious served with apple also.

Red Cabbage and Apple

(Pirates' Delight)

for two children or pirates

½ small red cabbage (use the rest grated in salads for yourself or the children)
1 small apple, peeled and cubed
2 tbsp. honey
1 tbsp. soaked raisins
½ cup water
1 small onion chopped
1 tbsp. lemon juice

Chop cabbage quite finely and cook all ingredients over medium heat for 40 minutes.

This is not a vegetable that is served often to children. But it is usually very popular. It can be served hot or cold. Too few of us realise that the red cabbage is not half as strong in flavour as the green, and gentler on little stomachs too. Try it in salads grated instead of green cabbage.

Cook cauliflower in milk to take away the strong flavour and to keep the beautiful white colour. Always remember to cook at low heat. Boiling vegetables does not make them cook more quickly and certainly does not improve their vitamin content. In fact, it destroys it.

Yellow turnip, broccoli, egg plant, peeled and cut into cubes are delicious cooked in milk.

Try adding wheat germ to many of your vegetables before you serve them. This imparts a delicious nutty flavour to them, and has the advantage of adding additional vitamins.

Sweet bell peppers are rich in Vitamin C and should be eaten frequently. I did not know for years that when ripe they are red, so whenever possible buy the red ones as their Vitamin C content is doubled.

Sauteed Bell Peppers

for two children

2 medium size sweet bell peppers
½ cup cubed mild cheddar cheese
2 tbsp. soya oil or oil of your choice

1. Cut peppers into small pieces.

2. Heat oil in pan.

3. Sauté slowly for 8 to 10 minutes. Peppers should still be crisp.

4. Just before serving, add cheese.

Beetroot Tops

bunch of green tops from young beets
1 tbsp. fresh lemon juice
1 tbsp. butter
¼ cup water

1. Wash beet tops.

2. Steam for 20 minutes.

3. When cooked, chop up fine and add lemon juice and butter.

Advantages: Loaded with iron, much more than spinach, and beneficial nutritionally more than the beet root.

Beet Roots

2 medium size beet roots
½ cup milk

1. Peel and cut beets into cubes.

2. Simmer gently in milk for 20 minutes.

Serve as is, or make sauce from the milk by adding some melted butter mixed with flour.

Green Bean Pie
(Like a Tamale Pie)

½ cup hot milk
1½ tbsp. butter
½ tbsp. chopped onion or leek
1¼ cups freshly cooked green
    beans, chopped very fine or
    blended in blender
1 egg, well beaten

1. Stir hot milk, melted butter and finely chopped onion or leek into chopped, cooked, green bean mixture.

2. Add beaten egg and blend well.

3. Pour into oiled dish and place in a pan of hot water.

4. Bake in 350° oven for 30 minutes.

This "pie" is done when the knife inserted into it comes out clean.

This has a custard-like texture and is a great favourite of the young toddler and child as well.

Cabbage Casserole

1 small cabbage
½ cup milk
2 ozs. grated cheese
1 tbsp. butter
2 tbsp. raisins that have been
    soaked overnight.

1. Shred cabbage very fine and cook in milk till tender. Do not cook at full rolling boil.

2. When cooked, drain off milk residue and keep for sauces and put cabbage into oiled casserole.

3. Sprinkle cheese, raisins, and butter on top.

4. Cook in moderate oven at 350° for 20 minutes, and finish by browning the top in the last few minutes.

Salads

Sunlight Food

Don't dismiss salads as something your child will learn to eat when he is older. Salads aren't just a few limp lettuce leaves and a sorry-looking tomato. Flavours and consistencies are countless. I have already suggested how even the infant can start eating salads in a form acceptable to him. As your child becomes older, be prepared to introduce slowly the various leaf vegetables and fruits that go into the making of a salad. By the time he is about two years old, he should expect a salad either at lunch or supper, or at both. One- and two-year olds often find the texture of lettuce and other salad ingredients not to their liking. However, when my children were two years old, they suddenly started to demand more and more salads.

The Bibb and Boston lettuce, which we are so fond of in our home, were too "slippery" a texture for Suzanne; and she cut her teeth, so to speak, on iceberg lettuce. There are many other grated salad vegetables that children love and will eat from an early age: Grated carrots, turnips, yams, cabbage (especially red cabbage), kohlrabi, zucchini, celery, radishes, ground artichokes, peppers, and many others. Chopped tomatoes, apples, raisins, bananas, avocados, as well as your favourite berries in season make delightful additions to your salads. Lemon juice and oil make a great yet simple salad dressing — so does tomato juice. Of course, you can make your own combinations of salad dressings as long as they are not too highly spiced for young palates.

Always keep your salad greens in a plastic bag in the crisper of your fridge. This helps to retain valuable vitamins, many of which are lost when greens are left exposed to the air. Wash and dry vegetables as quickly as possible. Tear, rather than cut and shred for salads. Salads have the built-in advantage of being a natural finger food for young children.

In preparing a salad, remember to put the dressing on just before serving; otherwise if you pour it on too early, you will have a nasty, wilted, slimy salad that no adult will want to eat — let alone a child. The ideal way is to put only the oil in first, and when you are sure all the greens are coated, then add the lemon juice or vinegar. For most of my salads, I use 2 tbsp. of oil to 1 tbsp. of lemon juice or cider vinegar. If pure apple cider vinegar is used, there is no harm in a child having it.

Children love funny arrangements of foods. Even the most finicky eater will perk up at a smiling clown's face made of fruit salad, or a house with windows all made of salad. Use your own ingenuity. To introduce him to lettuce my husband says his mother made him parcels of lettuce which contained a little brown sugar and grated apples. But each mother usually has her own games and inventions.

Try greens other than the conventional lettuce leaf for salads. There are cabbage, spinach, dandelion greens, sprouts, lambs quarters, watercress, and parsley. Grated nuts can turn a simple salad into a full-fledged meal containing all the protein your child needs. Sesame seeds or soya nuts which have been toasted previously are great for scattering on salads, as are raisins, bits of cheese, tomatoes, peaches, cauliflower flowerets which have been parboiled first, cold cooked beet cubes, cucumbers, asparagus, sticks of carrot, turnips, shoestring potatoes, chopped leeks, sliced bananas, and a host of other fruits and vegetables which your children enjoy.

Sprouts in Your Kitchen

Sprouts are a very important addition to your salad bowl and your nutrition. Not Brussels sprouts, but seeds which can be grown in your kitchen all year around. They don't require soil or supplements, just water and a little tender care. Delicious in salads, sandwiches, sprinkled on soups or casseroles or vegetables or eaten as they are, they provide vitamins, protein, enzymes, minerals, and in some cases necessary polyunsaturated fatty acids. As a side benefit, a sprouting seed is a botany lesson to any child.

Remember to buy only certified organically grown seeds as many of the commercial varieties have chemicals sprayed on them. They are not difficult to obtain. Some supermarkets, and certainly health stores, have them. What kind of seeds to buy? Try alfalfa, soya beans (particularly crisp and loved by children), mung beans (they are the sprouts served with Chinese food), mustard, cress, wheat, barley, green peas, lentils, chick peas, lima beans, and sunflower seeds. And many others.

To grow sprouts you can buy one of the efficient commercial plastic-tiered trays which will take the guessing out of it all. But you can do just as good a job if you soak a few tablespoonfuls of seeds overnight and drain them the next morning. Keep them in a container which can be drained easily. Drain daily after the few tablespoons of water have been added. The water should be lukewarm and not too cold. A good method of draining the seeds is to put a piece of muslin or nylon over the mouth of the container and tip upside down gently. Be sure to keep the water. It is rich in minerals and can be used in soups or gravies.

Usually the sprouts are ready to "harvest" in four to five days. Try them on cereal; and I sometimes add them to a batch of bread I am making.

Don't be surprised if you find the children filching them, because what better salads can they have? Surplus seedlings can be kept in the fridge in a screw topped jar, or in a plastic bag in your crisper container.

Salad Dressing for Children

Lemon Dressing

1 tbsp. fresh lemon juice
(or ½ lemon and ½ cider vinegar)
3 tbsp. soya oil or oil of your
   choice
1 tsp. grated lemon peel.

Mix vigorously with fork and
sprinkle over salad just before
serving.

Easy-to-make Homemade Mayonnaise

½ cup oil
1 egg yolk
pinch of salt
pinch of mustard
1 tbsp. lemon juice or apple cider
   vinegar
a little grated lemon peel

1. Break egg yolk into blender
and add a little oil.

2. Add mustard, salt, and vinegar
or lemon juice.

3. Cover blender and blend at
low speed.

4. Immediately uncover and
pour in remainder of oil slowly.

5. Then add lemon peel.

6. Makes a little over half a cup.

It is economical to make more than this quantity and keep in a screw
topped jar. Use for salads, fillings for sandwiches, on eggs, and for fruit
salads. Add parsley or dill to it for "green goddess" dressing.

Tomato Dressing

3 tbsp. soya oil or oil of
   your choice
2 tbsp. tomato or V-8 juice
a little chopped parsley or dill
   or both

Mix and whip with a fork.
Saturate salad just before serving.

Many mothers have problems with children who are hungry between meals. That's a good time to offer them fruit. I make it a strict rule that no cookies are given at home between meals. But I always am willing to let the children have an apple, orange, pear, or other fruit. This does not fill their stomachs and dissuade them from their regular meals, neither does it stuff them with calories. Carrot sticks and celery sticks are good, too, for those in-between meal snacks.

 Drinks

In addition to the delicious natural fruit drinks we have available to us in this country (especially juice made with a juicer), sometimes there are occasions when your children would like a change, such as for parties, special treats, or after an illness. It does not have to be soft drinks which are full of sugar and take away the appetite. As a matter of fact, it need never be soft drinks. Here are a few recipes you might find interesting and tasty.

Children can drink tea without it doing any harm (and it makes them feel "grownup") if they drink herbal teas. There are many on the market and most of the flavours are so delicate that children really do enjoy them. I serve mine with honey and occasionally with milk in them. Try tasting the tea with and without so you can make up your own mind.

Camomile Tea Delicious. Has the fragrance of newly mown hay in a meadow and tastes very mild. Good for settling little stomachs after lots of excitement or just nice to drink.

Mint Tea Most children love mint tastes of any kind and this is usually no exception.

Fennel Tea Quite a strong flavour of liquorice. Mmm. Good.

Rose Hip Tea Red in colour, loaded with Vitamin C and very pleasant to drink, especially with a little honey added.

Linden Blossom Tea Known in our house as "magic flower tea".

Fruitee Mixture of orange peel, lemon and rose hips. A favourite with grownups too.

Mid Morning Tigers Milk

for two

In blender put
1 cup homo milk or soya milk
¼ cup fruit such as banana,
 pineapple, or berries in
 season.
½ tbsp. vegetable oil of your
 choice
¼ cup non-instant powdered
 milk
¼ cup brewers' yeast
2 tbsp. honey

Blend together all ingredients.

During the winter months this is a valuable source of vitamins for your whole family.

Simon's Summer Drink

for two

1¼ cups homo or soya milk
¼ cup coconut powder
1 tbsp. maple syrup or honey
1 tbsp. carob powder
1 tbsp. brewers' yeast

Blend everything together and enjoy.

Instant Lunch

½ cup apple juice
1 egg
2 dates
½ apple
1 tsp. brewers yeast

Blend in blender.

Serves one.

Egg Nog for the Younger Set

for two

1½ cups of homo or soya milk
1 whole egg yolk
1 tbsp. honey
1 tbsp. brewers' yeast
1 small banana

Blend together in the blender. Especially good for the child who has been loath to eat for a while.

Banana Shake

for two

1 ripe banana
1 cup soya or homo milk
1 tbsp. honey

Blend in blender. Pleasing fruit flavour.

Orange Milk Shake

for two

1 cup homo or soya milk
½ cup fresh orange juice
1 tbsp. honey

1. Add honey to the orange juice.

2. Whip into the cold milk or blend in blender.

Quite thick drink with the consistency of malted milk.

Malt Milkshake

for two

1 cup milk, soya or homo milk
3 tbsp. pure malt extract
1 tbsp. honey or maple syrup

Whizz everything in the blender. Delicious natural malt shake. One scoop of plain ice cream can be added if desired.

Lime Ambrosia

1½ cups pineapple juice
juice of one lime
1 strip of lime rind
½ cup maple syrup or honey
1 pint vanilla ice cream

1. Cover and blend for 10 seconds in blender.

2. Remove cover and gradually add 1 pint vanilla ice cream.

3. Blend until the mixture is smooth.

I have always made a large quantity of this as I find once it is made the adults in the household want it too, especially on a hot afternoon.

Paul's Prune Flip

1 cup milk
4 pitted cooked prunes
¼ cup prune juice
1 tsp. honey

Cover and blend at high speed until smooth.

Tomato Juice Cocktail

1 slice of onion
1 thick slice of green pepper
1 small stick of celery
¼ tsp. parsley
1½ cups tomato juice

Blend in blender. Serve with wedges of lemon.

Nog for the Small Ones

½ cup cranberry juice
½ cup milk
4 tbsp. cream
1 tsp. honey
½ cup crushed ice

Blend until frothy and let the children drink with the grown-ups.

Carrot Milk Beverage

1 cup soya milk or other milk
2 carrots cut into small pieces

1. Place in blender and liquefy.

2. Serve chilled, or heat gently and serve in mugs. Great for the little ones.

Serves two.

Orange Punch

¾ cup fresh orange juice
1 egg yolk
1 tbsp. wheat germ
1 tbsp. honey

Blend and drink!

Watermelon Cooler

Juice of one lime
1 cup fresh orange juice

1. Fill blender container halfway with seeded chunks of watermelon.

2. Add juice.

.3. Blend till smooth.

4. Add more watermelon if desired.

Even the littlest one in the family can have a few spoonfuls of this.

For those growing youngsters who never seem to get enough in the morning.

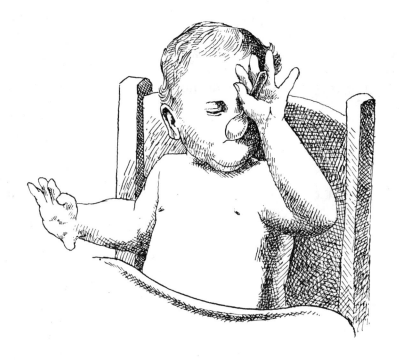

Soups and Casseroles

Soups are so often thought of as only an accompaniment to a main meal, whereas they can be a meal in themselves. If you have not tried your hand at making, concocting and cooking your own soups, you have missed a very satisfying experience. Soups have the added advantage of being a favourite "child" food. An imaginative mother can take a basic recipe, add to it or subtract, use an interesting garnish, and serve her very own soup a *la maison*. In the winter thick vegetable soups made from meat or vegetable stock go over very well, and are nutritious too. And summer soups can be a delicious change from the run-of-the-mill menu for lunch.

Don't overcook your vegetables. Chopping them up small adds to the flavour and takes less cooking time. Twenty minutes or so is enough time for cooking chopped vegetables for soup. Stock can be made days ahead and kept in the fridge for use in soups, sauces, and for additions to casseroles and gravies.

Your butcher can usually provide you with bones having plenty of marrow in them. You will not always see them on display, so get into the habit of inquiring for them. Meat, if it is to be added to the soup should be ground fresh and added a short while before serving since it will cook quickly. It is not good to have large lumps of meat sailing around in the stock; it looks distasteful and the meat will probably be stringy. For the best nutritional results fresh meat is better.

Don't spurn the simple vegetable stock for good nourishing soups. When I'm in a hurry and have come home a little late to prepare a three-course lunch for the children, I quickly chop up 5 or 6 different kinds of vegetables, add a few egg noodles or some vegetable macaroni, drop all into boiling water, turn down to low boil for 20 minutes or so, add a flavourful vegetable or meat extract if no meat stock is available, and serve as is or blend, if the mood takes me. With grated cheese or chopped nuts on top and served with some homemade buns or bread, you have a nourishing and hearty meal for the children in 30 minutes.

I have given basic recipes for soups here but do try your own additions.

Basic Meat Stock

Bones, meat trimmings,
uncooked
2 quarts of water
¼ cup cider vinegar*
3 cups chopped parings from
vegetables, uncooked (these
can be saved for a few days if
stored in a plastic container
in the refrigerator)

1. Combine first three ingredients and simmer for 3 to 4
hours.

2. Add vegetables and boil
slowly for 15 minutes.

3. Remove from heat and strain
through a colander.

This stock can be frozen. Before freezing, remove any fat and throw
out. Use for soups, sauces, and general cooking for the children and
rest of the family.

*The calcium in the bones is dissolved more readily by the addition of
vinegar. If any odour remains, leave the pan lid off and bring to a full
rolling boil. As there is no vitamin content in bones, no harm is done by
boiling.

Basic Vegetable Stock

1. Bring water to boil and add
parings and peels.

2. Boil slowly for 25 minutes.

3. Strain.

Any vegetable water from
steaming or boiling
vegetables
plus saved peels and parings
2 quarts of water

This can be kept in the fridge and frozen if not to be used immediately.
Use as a base for broths, soups, sauces, and drinks. Vegetable flavour-
ing of the "meaty" type, i.e. Marmite, can be added when the soup is
made.

Chicken Stock

2 lbs. chicken wings*
1 lb. chicken backs
2 quarts of water

1. Wash and chop bones into small pieces.

2. Proceed as for Basic Meat Stock.

This is very economical and children enjoy chicken soup. Meat from the bones can be left in the soup, but be careful to remove all the bones before serving to small children. Skim off any fat before freezing or using.

*I used to use chicken necks from the supermarket till I read that this is the part which is injected with stibestrol.

Clam Chowder

A meal in itself

small can of clams (4-oz. size)
1 small onion
1 medium potato chopped fine
1 small slice of lean bacon
1½ cups milk
1 tbsp. flour
1 tbsp. butter
1 tbsp. chopped parsley

1. Saute onion in butter and add chopped potato.

2. Saute gently, then add flour and coat onions and potatoes thoroughly.

3. Add bacon cut up in squares, then milk.

4. Bring to slow boil.

5. Add clams.

Serve at once with garnish of parsley and fresh bread or muffins or bread sticks.

Vegetable Soups Without Meat

1 unpeeled carrot, medium size
1 unpeeled potato
1 leek or onion
1 stalk celery
¼ cup soya flour
1 tbsp. chopped parsley
1 tsp. sea salt
any leftover vegetables such as
　lima beans, peas, maybe a
　little freshly-chopped tomato

1. Chop finely the chilled vegetables. Sauté these vegetables either in fat from the meat stock or, if using only vegetable stock, sauté in a little oil in the soup pan.

2. Mix soya flour with a little of the stock. Put aside.

3. Add 1 quart stock.

4. Add soya flour mixture, parsley, sea salt, and leftover vegetables.

5. Bring slowly to a boil for 10 minutes; or boil stock first before adding the leftover vegetables if you are in a hurry.

Serve with fresh muffins or buns and grated cheese on top of soup.

Variations
Instead of these vegetables, sauté and add one or more of the following: string beans, yellow turnip, cauliflower, zucchini, broccoli, fresh tomatoes, kohlrabi, parsnips, peas. You will know how much your child will eat. These soups are to be used for a complete meal. If you need them only as an accompaniment, then make a smaller quantity or freeze the surplus. To make a cream soup of this basic vegetable soup recipe, simply add ½ cup non-instant powdered milk. This should not be boiled. It should be added by beating or blending just before serving. This not only improves the flavour of the soup, but it also adds to its nutritional value. This recipe can be used with meat stock or chicken stock.

Basic Cream of Vegetable Soup

1 small leek or small onion, chopped
1 cup milk
¾ to 1 cup shredded or liquified vegetables
¼ to 1/3 cup non-instant powdered milk

1. Sauté leek or onion. Add 1 cup milk and bring to a slow simmer.

2. Add shredded or liquified vegetables. Simmer for 10 minutes.

3. Five minutes before serving, add powdered milk and blend. (You can use a blender or beat with a hand whisk.) More milk can be added if too thick.

Never boil milk soups. Of course, shredding or liquefying the vegetables will cut down your cooking time. Garnish with nuts or chopped parsley or strips of uncooked tomato.

Cream of Carrot and Lemon Soup

Basic Cream of Vegetable Soup recipe.
1 cup grated carrots instead of mixed vegetables and just before serving add 1 tbsp. fresh lemon juice.

In fact the lemon juice should be added at the table since otherwise it may curdle. Add garnish of finely grated lemon peel.

Cream of Leek and Potato Soup

Basic recipe as above. Instead of
mixed vegetables, use 1 medium
potato (chopped or grated) and 1
medium leek, finely chopped.

Celery Chowder

2 cups of chopped celery, tops
  and all.
1 cup boiling vegetable stock
1 medium size raw potato, grated
1 tbsp. butter
1 tbsp. unbleached flour
1½ cups milk, scalded
salt to taste
1 hard boiled egg

1. Drop the celery into the boiling stock.

2. Add potato and let simmer
until celery is tender and potato
is cooked, about 20 minutes.

3. Combine the butter and the
flour in another saucepan.

4. Beat in milk and gradually
bring to a boil and stir till mixture thickens.

5. Add salt, and stir into celery
mixture.

6. Add the chopped egg, and
simmer until mixture thickens.

Serve immediately with muffins or new bread.

Summer Soup (#1)

3 cups orange juice
2 whole cloves
¼-in. stick cinnamon
2 tbsp. cornstarch
1 tbsp. fresh lemon juice
1 cup strawberries
½ package frozen strawberries
1 ripe banana, sliced
½ cup green grapes

1. Put ¼ cup orange juice aside and heat the rest in a saucepan with the cloves and the cinnamon.

2. Heat to boiling and simmer for 5 minutes.

3. Blend cornstarch with remaining orange juice and add to the hot juice.

4. Cook for a further 5 minutes until the bubbles appear. Remove from heat and stir in the lemon juice.

5. Pour into a bowl and chill.

6. Remove spices with a slotted spoon and just before serving, add fresh strawberries and thawed ones too.

7. Sugar to taste if you wish but it is usually not necessary. Add bananas and grapes and serve. Mmmm...

You can substitute other fruits for the fruits in season.
Make plenty of this soup as it is a favourite with everyone.

Summer Soup (#2)

1 ripe canteloupe melon
1 orange peeled
1 tbsp. fresh lemon juice
yoghurt to garnish

1. Cut up melon and orange in chunks and put into blender.

2. Add lemon juice.

3. Garnish with yoghurt or slices of orange and lemon.

Watercress and Carrot Soup (Chilled)

1 bunch of watercress
1 cup shredded or grated carrots
1 small onion
1 cup milk
¼ cup non-instant powdered
  milk
1 tbsp. butter

1. Sauté onion and add carrot.

2. Sauté for a few more minutes.

3. Add milk and bring to boiling point.

4. Simmer gently for 5 minutes.

5. Blend in blender with powdered milk and washed • watercress.

6. Chill thoroughly and garnish with a little watercress or cucumber.

Cucumber soup can be made this way substituting cucumber for carrot.

Soya Bean Soup

1 cup cooked soya beans (see
   instructions for cooking)
   soya beans at the end of this
   chapter)
1 small minced onion or chopped
   leek
2 cups stock — vegetable,
   chicken or meat
¼ cup tomato puree or tomato
   paste
2 tbsp. butter
2 tbsp. flour

1. Press beans through sieve or blend in blender with a little stock.

2. Combine with tomato and return to pan.

3. Sauté leek and onion gently in butter in another pan and add flour.

4. Add to soup and stir till smooth and creamy.

5. Add salt if desired.

A very hearty soup. Serve with sandwich or rolls.

Tomato and Dill Soup

2 medium tomatoes
1 small onion or small leek
   chopped
salt to taste
1 or two sprigs of dill
1 tbsp. tomato paste
¼ cup cold water
¼ cup cooked brown rice or
   macaroni
½ cup milk
¼ cup non-instant powdered
   milk

1. Simmer the vegetables, tomato paste, and water for 15 minutes.

2. Pour into blender and add the rice or macaroni.

3. Turn on blender and gradually add the stock and the milks.

Great served chilled with topping of sliced tomato.
Note:
If you wish to serve hot, reduce milk to ¼ cup and increase stock to ¾ cup.

Tomato and Peanut Butter Soup

1 cup ripe tomatoes
1 small diced carrot
1 small diced onion
1½ cups stock
1 tbsp. butter
1 tbsp. flour
salt to taste
¼ cup unpasteurized peanut
   butter

1. Place all the ingredients ex-cept peanut butter, flour and butter in a pan and bring to boil.

2. Simmer for 20 minutes.

3. Press through sieve or blend in blender.

4. Return soup to pan.

5. Blend together the flour and butter in a small pan and add to soup.

6. Stir till soup thickens.

7. Just before serving add peanut butter and mix well.

The flavour will depend entirely on the quality of the peanut butter used.

Soup in the Blender

If you own a blender, there are so many different kinds of soups to be made for the family. Here are a few basic recipes from which a multitude of other soups can be concocted.

Basic Blender Vegetable Soup

½ cup chicken broth or
  vegetable stock
¼ cup leftover cooked potatoes
½ cup leftover cooked
  vegetables
1 tbsp. parsley
½ cup milk
1 small onion, chopped
¼ cup non-instant powdered
  milk

1. Into blender put onion and ¼ cup broth.

2. Cover and blend for 5 seconds.

3. Add remaining broth and vegetables.

4. Uncover and slowly pour in milk and milk powder.

5. To serve hot, heat to boiling point slowly and simmer 5 minutes.

Also good served chilled.

Cheese Soup

½ cup cubed mild cheddar
  cheese
1 tbsp. wholewheat flour
¼ cup chicken stock
¼ cup cream
1¼ cups milk
1 tbsp. butter
1 small clove of garlic
1 egg yolk

1. Heat 1 cup of milk, butter, and garlic in a saucepan.

2. Discard garlic.

3. Stir into the top of a double boiler the cheese, flour, remainder of milk, and just a suggestion of nutmeg.

4. Add the chicken stock.

5. Heat to boiling, and simmer for 15 minutes.

6. Just before serving stir in 1 egg yolk mixed with ¼ cup cream.

Great topped with a little more grated cheese.

Cream of Carrot Soup

2 fresh carrots washed and
  scraped
1 small onion
1 stalk of celery with leaves
¼ cup chicken stock
½ cup cooked brown rice, potato,
  or cooked pasta
½ cup milk
½ cup more chicken stock

1. Simmer for 15 minutes the two sliced carrots, onion, celery and ¼ cup chicken stock.

2. Empty into blender.

3. Add cooked rice.

4. Cover and blend for 10 seconds.

5. Add ½ cup chicken stock and ½ cup milk.

6. Pour into top of double boiler.

7. Heat to boiling and simmer for 15 minutes.

Serve hot or chilled with a garnish of lemon or orange slices.

Ideas for additional garnishes for soups   Thinly sliced apple rings, grated cheese, soya nuts, soya grits, peanuts, chopped almonds, chopped nuts of any sort, carrot curls, chopped celery, thinly sliced orange or lemon sections, chopped green onions, coconut, raisins, cucumber slices, avocado slices.

Casseroles

Of all the so-called meat substitutes we hear of, there is really none more worthwhile than the soyabean. Though it is inexpensive and a great source of protein for growing children and adults alike, it is often ignored because of its unglamorous associations. True, soyabeans take more cooking time than ordinary beans, but when you consider that they are made up of three times more protein than other beans, very little sugar, and no starch, you will begin to realise some of their merits.

The soyabean contains all the B vitamins, calcium and amino acids. To cut down on the cooking time, it is a great help to freeze the beans in their own liquid after they have been soaked and before they are to be cooked. This way you will cut down their cooking time by two hours.

Cooked Soyabeans

¾ cup dried soyabeans
1 tbsp. vegetable oil
pinch salt
½ cup tomato puree or paste
2 tbsp. honey or molasses
1 medium chopped onion

1. Soak soyabeans for two hours in 1 cup of water.

2. Place in freezing compartment and freeze overnight, till solid.

3. Remove and drop into ¾ cup hot stock.

4. Cook slowly for 2 to 3 hours. Add more stock if needed.

5. When nearly tender, add vegetable oil, salt, tomato puree or paste, honey or molasses, and chopped onion.

6. Continue cooking until tender. These beans are now ready to serve as is or can be ground up for casseroles, "meat" loaves, or patty burgers.

Soyabean and Nut Loaf

1 cup soyabeans cooked, as in previous recipe
¼ cup ground almonds
¼ cup ground cashews
1 tbsp. sesame seeds
½ tbsp. vegetable oil
¼ cup chopped celery
¼ cup chopped onion
¼ tsp. oregano
½ tsp. chopped parsley

1. Preheat the oven to 350°.

2. Put the beans through a meat grinder or use the "grind" cycle of your blender.

3. Mix in the nuts, and sesame seeds.

4. Heat the oil and sauté the celery and onions till tender.

5. Add to bean mixture with remaining ingredients.

6. Put into small loaf pan and bake for one hour.

(This mixture can also be shaped into patties and sauteed in a little oil.) (Make a vegetable extract-flavoured gravy to serve with the loaf or patties. Remember that soyabeans are pure protein and therefore very filling. I usually find that I do not need any more than one other vegetable with this, and sometimes not that.

Soyabean Casserole

1 cup cooked soyabeans
2 tbsp. honey
¼ cup tomato paste
¼ cup vegetable stock
¼ cup chopped green onion

1. Mix all ingredients.

2. Place in oiled casserole and cook in the oven for 45 minutes at 325°.

3. Add a little more stock if necessary.

These are textured and flavoured like good old Boston Baked beans. Great on toast or just as is.

Broiled Soyabean cakes

1 cup cooked soyabeans as recipe
½ cup diced celery with leaves
¼ cup cooked brown rice
¼ cup cooked chopped green onion
1 egg
2 tbsp. butter
¼ cup wheat germ
pinch of salt
¼ cup chopped green pepper
parsley sprigs and tomato slices

1. Blend soyabeans in blender or put through meat grinder.

2. Mix with celery, rice, onion, butter, wheat germ, green pepper, and salt.

3. Mix very well and form into patties.

4. Broil until golden and turn, and do other side.

5. Garnish with parsley and tomato slices.

6. Serve on whole wheat buns or bread slices.

These can be served with chipped potatoes, just like hamburgers.

Vegetable Pasta

Macaroni is a food small fry always enjoy and for those of you who have not yet tried the vegetable macaronis made with spinach, tomatoes, soya flour, carrots, etc., I suggest you do. A lot of the supermarkets are carrying these noodles and macaronis and the added advantages are that they contain little or no flour, but are usually vegetable based with soya or buckwheat flour and eggs. They are much lighter in texture and more colourful, and deliciously flavoured. If they are not available in your local supermarket, try your local health food store.

Wonderful Macaroni and Cheese

½ cup spinach or carrot
   macaroni
½ cup grated mild cheddar
   cheese
1 whole egg
1 small onion or leek chopped
   fine
1½ cups milk
½ cup water

1. Cook macaroni in water till soft.

2. In an oiled casserole mix the other ingredients, being sure to beat the egg before adding.

3. Add milk last.

4. Put in 300° oven and bake for one hour.

5. Last 5 minutes you can put under the broiler to form a golden crust.

Nut Casserole

½ cup nuts of your choice,
   ground as fine as you can
   (almonds, cashews, and
   filberts are good for this)
2 tbsp. flour
2 tbsp. butter
approximately 1 cup vegetable
   stock
2 tsp. vegetable extract such as
   Marmite

1. Melt butter and mix in flour over low heat.

2. Gradually add vegetable water and extract, stirring constantly.

3. When of desired thickness take from heat and add nuts. (Do not ever cook nuts, as this makes them practically indigestible.)

4. Now take your child's favourite combination of freshly cooked, mashed vegetables and line a casserole with them.

5. Pour the nut mince over the top and serve.

Yield: 2 servings.

Good combinations of vegetables are: potato and carrot; potato, carrot and turnip; turnip and carrot; sprouts, potatoes and carrots. This meal has the added advantage of being very high in protein content, and inexpensive to prepare. Nut mince can be served with toast or as a sauce for vegetables.

Shepherd's Pie Casserole

½ lb. chopped lean meat (ie; stewing beef put through the meat grinder yourself to eliminate all that surplus fat; or round steak done the same way)

1 medium onion or leek chopped
  and sautéed in 1 tbsp. butter
1 tbsp. flour
1 cup stock

1. Brown meat and add sauteed onion and flour.

2. Add stock and simmer for 30 minutes.

3. In the meantime, steam two medium size potatoes in their jackets for 30 minutes.

4. When potatoes are done, skin and mash with a little milk.

5. Line casserole with meat and top with potato. (Mashed carrots and turnips can be added if desired.)

6. Make pattern on top with fork and pop into 350° oven for 30 minutes.

7. Brown the last 5 minutes.

Grated cheese can be used as an extra special topping.

Yield: 4 servings.

Moussaka, (my version)

½ lb. ground beef
1 onion chopped
1 medium size eggplant or
   three baby ones
soya oil for cooking
2 tbsp. tomato puree or paste
6 ozs. stock
salt

Topping

1 egg
1½ tbsp. wholewheat flour
1 small container natural yoghurt
   or homemade yoghurt
   (approx. 5 ozs.)

1. Slice the eggplant and lay it on paper towelling. Sprinkle with salt and leave for 30 minutes.

2. Blot up excess salt and moisture and preheat oven to 350°.

3. Sauté eggplant in oil till transparent and line oiled casserole with some of the slices and put others aside.

4. Lightly fry the onions and put aside.

5. Then brown the meat.

6. Make layers of eggplant, onions and meat.

7. Mix puree and stock together and pour over.

8. Bake in oven for 45 minutes.

9. Make topping by beating egg well and adding flour and yoghurt.

10. Pour topping onto casserole and cook a further 15 minutes.

Yield: 4 servings.

The traditional Moussaka is much more complicated, but this is a pretty good substitute and nutritious too. If necessary, for healthy appetites, this can be served with brown rice. But it is very good alone, too.

double this

Beef Casserole with Dumplings

½ lbs. good stewing beef, cubed
1 medium onion or leek chopped
1 cup stock   *OXO Beef*
2 tbsp. flour
2 tbsp. oil *margarine*
pinch of oregano and parsley
salt
½ tsp. paprika

1. Dredge meat in flour. (An easy method is to put cubed meat and flour into a plastic bag and shake.)

2. Sauté onions in oil.

3. Add meat and brown.

4. Then add herbs and stock.

5: Place in casserole. Cover and cook for one hour at 350°

cook at 275°
all afternoon
turn up to 350°

6. For the last 20 minutes add dumplings, dropped in from spoon.

7. Cover and leave.

for dumplings

Dumplings

4 tbsp. wholewheat or
   unbleached flour
1 tbsp. vegetable oil
1 egg
1 tsp. baking powder
milk to mix

1. Beat egg.

2. Add flour, baking powder, oil, and enough milk to bind into a sticky soft paste.

3. Then drop onto the stew in the oven.

Serve as is with carrots, or turnip, or vegetables of your choice.

Yield: 4 servings.

Carrot Casserole

1¼ cups finely diced carrots
1 small onion or leek, chopped
¼ cup water
salt
1 tbsp. raw sugar or honey
¼ cup soy grits
1 tbsp. fresh chopped dill
1 egg lightly beaten
¼ cup sliced almonds

1. Place carrots, onion, water, and salt in saucepan.

2. Bring to a boil and simmer until carrots are tender, about 15 minutes.

3. Preheat oven to 350°

4. Stir honey or sugar, dill weed, and egg into cooked carrot mixture. If necessary, lightly mash and mix well.

5. Turn into oiled baking dish and sprinkle with almonds. Bake 15 minutes.

Yield: 4 servings.

Noodle Casserole

4 ozs. wholewheat, spinach, or
   carrot noodles
½ cup cottage cheese or ricotta
   cheese
½ cup yoghurt
salt
1 egg, lightly beaten
¼ cup parmesan cheese, freshly
   grated if possible
1 tbsp. chopped parsley or
   tomato

1. Preheat oven to 300°.

2. Mix together everything except the noodles.

3. Cook and drain noodles.

4. Add cheese mixture and toss.

5. Turn into a buttered casserole and bake for 45 to 60 minutes.

Yield: 2 servings

Carrot Loaf

1 cup raw grated carrots
¾ cup cooked brown rice
½ cup peanuts or cashews
1/3 cup raw peanut butter
¾ cup soya milk
½ tsp. sage
1 egg, lightly beaten

1. Preheat oven to 325°.

2. Mix together the carrots, rice and nuts.

3. Blend together the soya milk and peanut butter, either with a whisk or blender.

4. Add sage and eggs.

5. Pour milk mixture over carrot mixture and mix well.

6. Turn into oiled casserole and bake 45 minutes or till set.

Tuna Fish Casserole

1 small tin of tuna fish (use best grade, packed in soya oil if possible)
½ cup soya macaroni
1 small peeled tomato
1 oz. grated mild cheddar cheese
½ cup water or vegetable stock
1 egg beaten
1 cup milk
1 green onion, chopped

1. Cook macaroni till soft.

2. In casserole mix tuna fish, beaten egg, chopped tomato, onion, and milk.

3. Sprinkle grated cheese over top.

4. Bake for 45 minutes at 325°.

Yield: 4 servings.

Tuna Fish Treat with Cucumber Sauce

1 6-oz. can of tuna
1 beaten egg
¼ cup milk
1 tbsp. butter
¼ cup chopped onion
1 tbsp. chopped parsley
¼ tsp. basil

1. Combine egg, milk, butter, onion, parsley, and seasonings.

2. Break tuna into chunks and stir into egg mixture.

3. Pour into small oiled casserole.

4. Bake at 425° for 25 minutes.

Yield: 4 servings.

Cucumber Sauce

1 small cucumber, unpared
½ tsp. grated onion
¼ cup mayonnaise
1 tbsp. lemon juice
1 tbsp. chopped parsley
¼ cup sour cream
salt

1. Cut cucumber lengthwise, scoop out seeds, and grate.

2. Drain.

3. Combine ingredients and chill. (If desired the cucumber can be peeled.)

Serve with casserole and slices of tomatoes.

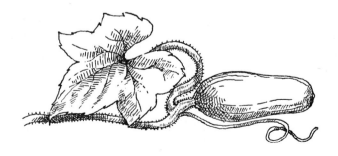

Chicken and Egg Casserole

¾ slice wholewheat bread, crumbled
¼ cup milk
1½ cups finely diced cooked chicken
1 tsp. minced onion
¼ tsp. salt
1 tbsp. chopped parsley
2 tbsp. oil or butter
1 whole egg and 1 yolk
1 tbsp. lemon juice freshly squeezed (optional)

1. Preheat oven to 350°

2. Soak the bread in the milk. Add chicken, onion, salt, parsley, and oil or butter.

3. Beat the 2 egg yolks well and add.

4. Beat egg white till stiff, but not dry, and fold into mixture.

5. Pour into oiled souffle or casserole dish and set in pan of boiling water.

6. Bake until set, about 30 minutes.

7. Pour the lemon juice over the casserole just before serving.

Yield: 4 servings.

Glorious Rice Casserole

1 cup cooked brown rice
½ cup grated cheddar cheese
½ cup milk
1 egg beaten
½ cup vegetable water
1 tbsp. melted butter
1 tbsp. parsley
1 small onion, chopped
1 oz. slivered almonds
1 oz. sesame or sunflower seeds

1. Combine all ingredients except nuts and sunflower seeds.

2. Turn into oiled casserole.

3. Top with nuts.

4. Bake 30 minutes at 350°.

5. Garnish with seasame seeds, sunflower seeds, and nuts.

Yield: 4 servings.

Spaghetti and Sauce

For two

Use spinach, tomato, or vegetable noodles, which are made of soya flour and so are much lighter, and of course not so starchy.

Sauce

1 small onion or leek
3 medium size tomatoes, chopped
1 medium pepper, chopped and seeded
1 zucchini, washed and chopped
¼ lb. mushrooms, washed and chopped
2 tbsp. sunflower seeds
1 tbsp. sesame seeds
1 tbsp. chopped parsley
1 stick of celery, chopped
1 tsp. fresh basil
1 small carrot, chopped
1 cup vegetable stock
salt optional

1. Combine all ingredients in pan and bring to boil.

2. Simmer for 25 minutes.

3. If beef is desired, brown ¼ lb. ground beef and add to the sauce for the last 10 minutes of simmering.

Meanwhile, cook noodles or spaghetti and drain.

This sauce is also great with chopped chicken added last. Grated cheese sprinkled over the top of the sauce is good.

For sea food lovers, add a small tin of drained clams after sauce is cooked, or ¼ lb. shrimp.

Meat, Poultry and Fish

Meat is an important part of the growing child's diet, as it is pure protein and contains all the amino acids and B vitamins. What a lot of us don't realise is that much of the nutritive value is lost by cooking at high temperatures. You probably won't be cooking a whole roast for your child, but when you next cook a roast, try lowering the temperature considerably. For instance, try your next beef roast at 250 as opposed to the usual 350 to 450 . Multiply the cooking time by three and with this lower temperature you will have a much tenderer roast and will have saved much more of the valuable vitamins and amino acids. High temperatures will give you tough meat, as they destroy the protein content.

You do not need always to buy the most expensive meats to get the best protein content and tenderest cuts. I often buy stewing steak from a good butcher who cuts it freshly for me, then I grind it up myself for hamburgers, meat loaves, casseroles, etc. And it is always good. If possible, always have your butcher grind your meat for you or do it yourself. I never buy plastic covered stewing beef or ground meats. Too much fat is hidden by the plastic and you never can be quite sure how old it is. Our meat is being subjected to all kinds of hormone injections today and tenderizers are fed the beast for a more tender cut.

Where this will all end we do not know and we have to make do with the supply we have. Some of us are lucky enough to be able to buy meat from a reliable source where we are fairly sure that no injecting has been done. The best thing you as a mother can do is always to try to get the best possible and freshest meat that your butcher can supply. If in doubt, don't buy. There are other sources of protein which can be utilised.

Marinating cheaper cuts of meat, even for children, is a good way of breaking down the tissues and ensuring tenderness. Cider vinegar is a good base for a marinade, and providing it is a pure apple cider vinegar it will not be bad for the children. Marinating simply means soaking for a few hours in a mixture of your choice, with a base of an acid such as vinegar or lemon juice, or for the adults, wine. It does not have to be highly spiced for the younger set and can be very enjoyable.

I do not give my own children meat every day. They have other sources of protein. Besides meat there is fish, poultry, nuts, and grains. I give them meat probably twice a week. I have included some of their favourite beef recipes which I hope you will enjoy.

Meat Pies

Wholewheat pastry (see
   page 122)
½ lb. lean stewing beef cut in
   inch cubes
¼ lb. beef kidney, trimmed of fat
   and tissues and cut up
1 medium onion
2 mushrooms
2 tbsp. oil
1 cup vegetable or beef stock
½ tsp. oregano
2 tbsp. flour

1. Dredge meat and kidney in flour. (Use the plastic bag method here.)

2. Brown in oil, and add chopped onion.

3. Sauté a few minutes and add mushrooms, herbs, and stock.

4. Simmer either on top of the stove for one hour or in the oven in a casserole for one hour at 300

5. Meanwhile, make pastry as per method and line small pie pans or shallow muffin tins.

6. When filling has cooked and cooled, fill 2/3 full and put pastry top on.

7. Bake at 350° to 375° for 25 minutes and serve with the child's favourite vegetables.

This can be served as one pie with one crust in a casserole. And if desired, kidney can be eliminated.

Yield: 4 servings.

Potato Meat Loaf

½ lbs. ground round steak
¼ cup tomato juice
1 small onion finely chopped
½ cup finely grated or
   shredded raw potatoes
½ tbsp. chopped parsley
1 small carrot, shredded
1 egg lightly beaten
salt

1. Preheat oven to 375°.

2. Mix all the ingredients together and pack into small loaf tin which has been oiled.

3. Bake one hour or until done.

4. Serve with rich beef gravy or nut mince gravy.

Yield: 4 servings.

Meat Loaf

½ lbs. chopped beef
1 small onion finely chopped
1 small glove of garlic pressed
   (optional)
2 ozs. finely chopped cleery
1 small carrot, grated
1 tbsp. chopped parsley
1 tbsp. sesame seeds
1 tbsp. soya grits
½ cup milk
1 egg lightly beaten
2 tbsp. tomato puree or paste

1. Preheat oven to 325°.

2. In bowl combine beef, onion, garlic, celery, carrot, parsley, and sesame seeds.

3. Soak the grits in milk for two minutes.

4. Add to meat mixture with salt, eggs, and tomato puree or paste.

5. Put in oiled small loaf pan and bake for one hour.

Serve with or without gravy sauce and vegetables.

Yield: 4 servings

Liver For Liver haters

½ lbs. calves or beef liver
1 small onion
1 large apple, peeled and cored
  and cut into rings
½ cup stock
2 tbsp. oil or butter
1 tbsp. wheat germ.

1. Sauté liver and onions gently in butter or oil.

2. When cooked put through coarse mincer.

3. Add stock and mix well.

4. Line oiled casserole with this mixture.

5. Arrange 1 cup cooked mashed potatoes on top, and finish with apple slices.

6. Cook in 325° oven for 20 minutes. Serve right away.

Yield: 4 servings.

Marinated Steak

½ lb. of flank steak
  *(If you can obtain your beef
  from an organic source so
  much the better.)*
¼ cup soya sauce
1 tbsp. honey
1 tbsp. lemon juice
¼ tsp. ginger
1 clove garlic, chopped

1. Remove and discard any fat from the steak. Place steak in a ceramic dish.

2. Score the steak deeply with sharp knife.

3. Combine remaining ingredients and pour over steak.

4. Allow to marinate for 6 hours, turning frequently.

5. Drain steak and broil to desired degree of doneness. About 5 minutes on each side should do it. Serve with baked potato.

Yield: 4 servings.

Chicken

Chicken is always a favourite food with children, and it can be cooked in so many different ways. Providing you know where it came from, it can be a good source of protein. Those of us who are still able to go to a farmers' market and buy a plump, tender chicken that has been nourished on good grain and allowed to run free should be grateful. Chickens are being raised by millions in artificial atmospheres. They certainly are tender but just as certainly almost tasteless. There is a definite difference in the freshly killed farm chickens and the flaccid pieces of poultry sold in supermarkets. Anyway, the rule of thumb here is to buy the whole bird, if possible, and ask your butcher to cut it up for you. Do not buy the packaged products unless you know how old they are. Some of the deep frozen chickens are more tasty than the rest and probably a better buy nutritionally.

Chicken Breasts in Dill

2 small chicken breasts,
  preferably from source you
  know
2 tbsp. butter or oil
½ cup milk
3 sprigs fresh dill weed
2 tbsp. unbleached flour
2 tbsp. butter
grated lemon peel
2 tbsp. sesame seeds

1. Cut breast into four pieces.

2. Brush with the butter or oil.

3. Broil under the grill for 10 minutes.

4. Make sauce while chicken is cooking. Melt the 2 tbsp. butter, stir in flour, and add milk gradually till it thickens.

5. Add chopped dill weed.

6. Place chicken in casserole and pour on sauce.

7. Put in 300° oven for 30 minutes.

8. Just before serving sprinkle with lemon peel and sesame seeds.

Yield: 2 servings.

Sesame Baked Chicken

1 egg lightly beaten
¼ cup milk
ç cup wholewheat flour
salt
1 tbsp. sweet paprika
1 tbsp. sesame seeds
2 chicken breasts, (halved)
  or thighs
¼ cup melted butter

1. Preheat oven to 350°.

2. Beat the egg and milk together in shallow dish.

3. Combine flour, salt, paprika, and sesame seeds in a bag.

4. Dip the chicken in the egg mixture then shake in the bag.

5. Place chicken pieces skin side up in a baking dish so they do not touch each other.

6. Pour melted butter over and cook for one hour.

Chicken with Yoghurt

1 tbsp. butter
1 tbsp. safflower oil
½ frying chicken cut into pieces
½ cup chicken broth
1 tbsp. chopped chives
sea salt
1 tbsp. unbleached flour
¼ cup yoghurt

1. Heat butter and oil and fry chicken in it till golden brown.

2. Return all chicken to skillet.

3. Add broth and sprinkle with chives and salt.

4. Cover and cook over low heat for 20 minutes or until chicken is done.

5. Remove chicken to serving plate.

6. Remove any fat from broth.

7. Mix flour and yoghurt and add to skillet. Cook until thickened but do not boil. Pour over chicken and serve.

Yield: 4 servings.

Roast Chicken with Prune and Apple Stuffing

1 3- to 4-lb. roasting chicken, preferably from a farmer you know.

Roast your chicken at 300° for 1½ to 2 hours till golden brown.

Baste with own juice. Turn up to 350° last 30 minutes.

Meanwhile make the stuffing and add in the last 45 minutes of cooking.

Stuffing

1 cup pitted cooked prunes
3 apples
water to cover or vegetable stock
pinch of cinnamon

1. Retain the liquid from the prunes as fruit stock, and chop the prunes into small pieces.

2. Core and cut apples into small pieces, leaving skins on.

3. Mix both fruits.

4. Add cinnamon.

5. Stuff during the last 45 minutes.

Roast chicken is always popular. This recipe will probably serve a small family. If you are lucky enough to have one which scratched around for its living, this bird will yield a delicious pan gravy for serving with your chicken.

Chicken en Casserole

2 plump breasts or thighs of
  chicken
½ cup chicken stock
1 cup mushrooms finely sliced
1 small onion chopped fine
4 tbsp. butter or vegetable oil
¼ tsp. oregano
½ tsp. basil
2 tbsp. flour
2 tbsp. wheatgerm

1. Sauté gently the onions in the butter or oil.

2. Dredge pieces of chicken in flour and wheatgerm which have been mixed.

3. Fry the chicken until golden brown, on both sides.

4. Add mushrooms and stock.

5. Simmer for 10 more minutes, then transfer everything to a casserole for 30 minutes in 325° oven.

If desired, vegetable stock can be used instead of chicken stock.

Yield: 4 servings.

Fried Chicken

As many serving pieces of breasts, thighs, and legs as are needed.

oil to fry (safflower is my favourite)

wheat germ

Batter

1 to 2 eggs
2 to 4 tbsp. unbleached flour
¼ to ½ cup milk

1. Beat eggs.

2. Gradually add flour and milk. Batter should be thick.

3. Heat oil in pan. Do not have so much oil that the chicken is immersed.

4. Shake chicken pieces in a plastic bag in the wheat germ, and then dip in the batter.

5. Fry in the hot fat till golden brown on both sides.

6. Turn down heat.

7. Cover and cook at medium temperature for 20 minutes.

8. Drain on paper towelling.

If you are using soya, sesame, or safflower oils you will find very little residue of fat remaining on the paper. Children love chicken done this way. Serve with Oven French Fries.

You can use this same batter for frying fish.

Fish

Fish has as much protein content as meat, plus it is rich in phosphorus. Sea fish are a good source of iodine. Vitamins A & D are stored in the liver, which unfortunately is usually thrown out. All the B vitamins are present and are not lost in the cooking, providing care is taken with the temperatures. Steaming is a good gentle way of cooking fish, and broiling is popular with children but not the most nutritious way of serving it.

Fish is probably one of the most difficult foods to introduce to your child, but only because of lack of imagination. Of course there will always be the child who genuinely does not enjoy fish. The texture seems strange to the very young child. I found that my children were 18 months to 2 years old before they really seemed to enjoy it without having it disguised.

I find that some of the favourite fish dishes with my children are the ones which take the very minimum of preparation. By the way, in order to forestall having a fishy odour cling to your hands, before handling fish it is a good idea to wash your hands in ice cold water and rub in a little moist salt. After finishing preparation of the fish, wash your hands with hot water. This usually will do the trick. Fishy odours hanging around the kitchen can be avoided by not cooking or frying at high temperatures.

Fish Dishes

Fish Omelette

2 eggs
2 tbsp. butter
2 tbsp. cream
1 cup flaked, cooked, white fish
salt
1 tbsp. chopped parsley
slices of tomato

1. Break eggs into bowl and beat lightly.

2. Melt butter in omelette pan.

3. When quite hot, pour in eggs and cream and stir quickly to prevent sticking.

4. As soon as the mixture begins to set, sprinkle the flaked fish over it and start to shape the sides over into a double shape.

5. Cook lightly for one more minute, and then place on a hot platter and garnish with parsley and tomatoes. Serve at once.

Yield: 2 servings.

Grilled Fish With Summer Sauce

filleted lemon sole, plaice, turbot, haddock, or cod (allow approx. ½ lb. per child)
3 tbsp. butter
parsley and lemon for garnish

Summer Sauce

2 tbsp. butter
2 tbsp. unbleached flour
½ cup milk
½ cup chopped seedless green grapes
1 tbsp. grated lemon rind
1 tbsp. chopped parsley

Yield: 2 servings

1. Dry fish and dot with butter. Broil under hot grill for approximately 10 minutes.

2. While fish is broiling, make the sauce. Melt butter and blend in flour, stirring constantly.

3. Add milk slowly and stir over heat until sauce thickens.

4. Add rest of ingredients and warm gently for 3 minutes.

5. Pour sauce over grilled fish and serve immediately.

This sauce seems to be a great help to the children who aren't so keen on plain old fish. The rest of the family should try it too.

Another sauce which is a great favourite for pouring over grilled fish is known in our house as

Sara's Sauce for Fish

2 tbsp. butter
2 tbsp. unbleached flour
½ cup milk
½ cup small cooked BC shrimp
1 small skinned tomato, cut up
1 tsp. chopped parsley

1. Melt butter and blend in flour, stirring constantly.

2. Add milk slowly, stirring over heat till the sauce is the required thickness.

3. Then add parsley, tomato, and shrimp.

4. Serve right away over fish or a mixture of vegetables.

Cheese & Tuna Souffle

*(Made in the blender and ab-
solutely foolproof)*

Into blender container put the
following:
1 cup grated cheese (4 ozs.)
2 tbsp. butter
4 tbsp. unbleached white flour
¼ tsp. dry mustard
½ 6-oz. tin tuna, drained
    thoroughly
salt
5 egg yolks
1 cup hot milk

1. Cover, and blend on high
speed for 15 seconds.

2. Pour into saucepan and cook
over a low heat till smooth and
thick.

3. Fold in 5 stiffly beaten egg
whites.

4. Pour into 1½ quart oiled souffle dish and bake in a preheated
375° oven for 30 minutes.

5. Serve at once.

*Will serve 4 adults or 2 growing
children.*

Puffy Cheese and Salmon Omelette

(In blender again and just as foolproof)

Put the following into the blender:

1/3 cup milk
1 cup grated mild cheddar cheese
½ cup flaked fresh or tinned salmon
salt
6 egg yolks
¼ cup parsley leaves

1. Cover, and blend on high speed for 10 seconds.

2. Fold into 6 stiffly beaten egg whites.

3. Pour mixture into oiled greased omelette pan.

4. Spread evenly and cook over low heat until puffed and lightly browned underneath.

5. Transfer to a preheated 375° oven and brown the top.

Serves 4 adults.

Variations of this omelette can be made by substituting, shrimp, diced ham, diced chicken, green peppers, or tomatoes.

Cakes, Cookies and Pies

In our house we don't have an abundance of sweet stuff like cakes, cookies and pies. But what we have is usually home made. I find that today so many of the sweet cakes and cookies contain so many things undesirable for growing children that it is easier and more nutritious to make my own. Children will always love cookies and if they have the right ingredients they can contribute towards good health as much as any other food. I serve cakes and pies and cookies at mealtimes, and only occasionally, cookies between meals.

I am not a great cake maker and I find that special occasions such as parties and friends for tea are about the only time I make them, but they always disappear at a most alarming rate. Don't dismiss the idea of making your own cakes because it means too much work. Try it, and enjoy your flour power. Those oohs and aahs of appreciation are all the encouragement you'll need.

Banana Bread

1 cup brown sugar
3 large ripe bananas
4 tbsp. melted butter
1½ cups unbleached white flour
½ tsp. salt
1 tsp. soda
2 eggs

1. Mash bananas to a thin batter. Add the sugar and eggs.

2. Beat together well.

3. Add the melted butter, and then the flour which has been sifted with salt and soda.

4. Mix well.

5. Pour into a greased loaf pan.

6. Bake in a preheated oven at 375° for about 50 minutes.

Lemon Loaf Cake

This is more like a bread and can be served with or without butter.

2 tbsp. butter
1 cup brown sugar
2 eggs
1½ cups unbleached white flour
½ cup milk
2 tsp. baking powder
grated rind of one lemon
1 tbsp. fresh lemon juice
¼ cup chopped walnuts

1. Cream butter and sugar and add the eggs.

2. Mix in the dry ingredients.

3. Pour into a greased pan lined with wax paper, and let rise for 20 minutes.

4. Bake in a preheated oven at 350° for 45 to 50 minutes.

5. Remove from oven and while still hot, brush the top, sides, and bottom with lemon juice mixed with a little sugar.

Eccles Cakes

1 recipe of Flaky Pie Crust (See page 122)
½ cup currants
¼ cup chopped peel
¼ cup sugar
pinch of nutmeg
1 tbsp. melted butter

1. Mix fruit, sugar, nutmeg, butter and peel.

2. Roll pastry out to ¼ in. thick and cut into two-inch rounds.

3. Place tablespoons of mix on each round and gather up edges and seal firmly

4. Turn circles over with pinched side down.

5. Roll out until fruit starts to show through.

6. Mark tops of cakes in cross pattern.

7. Brush the cakes with egg white and dredge with sugar.

8. Bake in preheated oven at 425° for 10 to 15 minutes. Reduce heat to 350° and then test for readiness. Pastry should be crisp and lightly brown.

Yield: 8 cakes

Oatcakes

1 cup oatmeal
½ cup wholewheat flour
2 tsp. baking powder
2 tbsp. brown sugar
½ cup margarine
½ tsp. sea salt
4 tbsp. cold water

1. Sift the flour, salt, and baking powder into a bowl and add the oatmeal and sugar.

2. Rub in the margarine.

3. Mix with water to a firm consistency.
4. Knead lightly on an oatmeal sprinkled surface.

5. Roll out ¼ in. thick and cut into rounds.

6. Bake 15 minutes in preheated oven at 350°.

7. Cool and serve with butter, cheese, home-made jam or marmalade for breakfast.

Yield: 8 oatcakes.

Rich Brown Scones

(Strictly speaking these should not be included with "cakes," but in our house they are loved just as much.)

2 cups wholewheat flour
2 tsp. baking powder
½ tsp. salt
¼ cup margarine
2 tbsp. brown sugar
1/3 cup sultanas or raisins
1 egg
6 tbsp. milk

1. Mix flour and salt in a bowl and rub in the margarine.

2. Mix in the sugar and fruit.

3. Beat the egg and milk together and add to the flour to make a soft dough.

4. Turn onto a floured surface and roll out to ½ in. thickness.

5. Cut into two-inch rounds.

6. Place on a greased baking sheet and brush the tops with beaten egg and milk.

7. Bake at 425° for 10 minutes.

Yield: 12-16 scones.

Bannock Cakes

(A childhood treat which still is popular in our house)

2 cups wholewheat flour
½ cup butter
¼ cup brown sugar
¼ cup blanched almonds
¼ cup chopped peel

1. Chop almonds finely and mix with peel.

2. Knead butter and sugar, preferably on a wooden board to air it.

3. Sift flour, and work it into the butter with the peel and almonds.

4. Knead until smooth.

5. Shape the dough into an eight-inch round, ½ in. thick.

6. Place on lightly-greased tray and prick all over with a fork.

7. Bake in the middle of the oven at 320° for 40 to 45 minutes until light brown.

8. Sprinkle with sugar and allow to cool.

Rock Cakes

2 cups wholewheat or
   unbleached white flour
1 tsp. baking powder
½ cup brown sugar
½ cup margarine
½ cup currants or small raisins
3 tbsp. chopped citron peel
1 egg and a little milk

1. Mix the flour and sugar in a bowl, and then rub in the margarine.

2. Mix in currants and peel.

3. Mix to a stiff dough with the beaten egg and a little milk.

4. Place in rough heaps on a greased baking sheet.

5. Bake in a preheated oven 425° to 450° for about 20 minutes.

Yield: 16 cakes.

Granny Cake

2 cups wholewheat flour
1 tsp. baking powder
2 tbsp. brown sugar
½ cup chopped walnuts
½ cup raisins
1 tbsp. maple syrup or honey
5 tbsp. milk
pinch of salt

1. Place all dry ingredients together in a bowl and add the nuts and fruit.

2. Add the syrup or honey and milk.

3. Beat to a very soft mixture.

4. Place in a greased 8-inch cake tin.

5. Bake in a moderate oven at 350° for about 45 minutes.

6. Brush with Sugar Glaze while still warm.

Sugar Glaze

2 tbsp. brown sugar
1 tbsp. boiling water

Mix, and apply to hot cake with pastry brush.

Date & Walnut Cake

8 ozs. dates, pitted and chopped
pinch of soda
½ cup boiling water
1/3 cup margarine
1/3 cup brown sugar
1 egg
2 cups wholewheat flour
1 tsp. baking powder
½ cup broken walnuts

1. Break dates into small pieces and put in bowl.

2. Pour the boiling water with pinch of soda on the dates.

3. Leave until cool.

4. Cream margarine and sugar, and add beaten egg.

5. Mix in flour, nuts, and last, the dates.

6. Pour the mixture into a greased 2-lb. loaf tin or cake tin.

7. Bake at 325° for 1¼ hours.

Orange and Raisin Loaf

2 cups wholewheat or
  unbleached white flour
1 tsp. baking powder
½ tsp. soda
1 tbsp. margarine
½ cup brown sugar
grated rind and juice of 1 orange
2/3 cup seedless raisins
milk to mix

1. Mix flour, soda, and baking powder. Rub in the margarine.

2. Mix in sugar, grated orange rind, and raisins.

3. Place orange juice in measuring cup and make up ½ cup with milk.

4. Stir. (The batter is very thick.)

5. Spread mixture into cake tin, and make a depression in the centre to avoid a peaked cake.

6. Bake in a 350° oven for 20 minutes, and then in a 325 oven for 1¼ hours.

Very Favourite Sultana Malt Cake

2 cups wholewheat flour
1 tsp. baking powder
1 tsp. soda
2 tbsp. honey or maple syrup
2 tbsp. malt extract
1 cup milk
1 egg
½ cup sultanas or raisins

1. Sift flour and soda.

2. Mix honey or syrup, malt extract, and milk together.

3. Beat egg and add to flour with liquid mixture.

4. Add sultanas or raisins and pour mixture into greased one-pound loaf or cake tin.

5. Bake at 350° for 40 to 45 minutes.

Basic Sandwich Cake Recipe

(for parties)

½ cup margarine
½ cup white sugar
1 cup unbleached flour
1 tsp. baking powder
2 eggs

1. Cream margarine and sugar until light and creamy in texture.

2. Add eggs, a little at a time, and beat well.

3. Gently fold in flour mixed with baking powder.

4. Pour mixture into a greased 8-inch cake tin.

5. Bake in a moderate oven at 325° to 350° for 25 to 30 minutes.

6. When cool, slice cake in half horizontally and sandwich together with jam or whipped cream.

Queen Cakes

1. Make Basic Sandwich Cake recipe.

2. Add 1 tbsp. currants with the flour mixture.

3. Half fill muffin tins with mixture.

4. Bake at 350° for about 20 minutes.

Butterfly Cakes

1. Make Basic Sandwich Cake recipe.

2. Half fill paper baking cups with mixture.

3. Bake at 350° for about 20 minutes.

4. When cool, cut a slice from the top of each cake. Cut this in half.

5. Place a dab of yoghurt in each cavity and arrange wings on cake.

Variations

Jams, whipped cream, or applesauce can be used as a filling in place of the yoghurt.

"Chocolate" Layer Cake

1 cup milk, scalded
½ cup Carob* powder
1¼ cups brown sugar
1 tsp. allspice
2 eggs
1 tsp. vanilla
½ cup sunflower seed oil
pinch of salt
2¼ cups wholewheat flour,
   sifted
2 level tsps. baking powder

1. Scald the milk.

2. Blend the Carob, ½ cup sugar, and spice. Stir them gradually into the scalded milk.

3. Cool the mixture.

4. Combine ¾ cup sugar, eggs, vanilla, sunflower seed oil, and salt. Beat until very light and creamy.

5. Sift together the flour and baking powder.

6. To lthe egg and sugar mixture, add the Carob mixture alternately with the flour and baking powder.

7. Beat the batter for 2 or more minutes.

8. Bake at 350° for about 30 minutes in greased and floured 8-inch tins.

9. Ice with Seafoam Frosting. (See page 149)

*Use Carob as a substitute for chocolate and you'll find it just as flavourful. Carob powder can be bought in health stores and some supermarkets.

Carob Cake

(like chocolate, but made with Carob powder)

1¾ cups unbleached white flour
1 cup brown sugar
2 tbsp. Carob powder
¼ cup margarine
2 eggs beaten with 5 tbsp.
 evaporated milk
5 tbsp. water
1 tsp. vanilla

1. Sift together the flour, sugar, and Carob powder.

2. Rub in margarine.

3. Stir in eggs, vanilla, and liquids.

4. Beat well.

5. Grease and flour 2 8-inch layer cake tins.

6. Bake at 325° for 35 minutes.

7. When cool, sandwich together with Carob butter cream. For party occasions, ice top with frosting.

Carob Frosting

1/3 cup Carob powder
2/3 cup non-instant powdered
 milk
2 tbsp. oil
¼ cup honey
4 tbsp. top of the milk
1 tsp. pure vanilla extract

Mix.

Will frost one cake.

Walnut Cake

½ cup margarine
¼ cup brown sugar
1 tbsp. honey or maple syrup
1 egg
2/3 cup unbleached flour
1½ tsp. baking powder
2 tbsp. milk
¼ cup chopped walnuts
Large walnuts for top of cake

1. Cream margarine, sugar, and syrup until light and creamy.

2. Beat in the egg.

3. Gradually add flour, milk, and nuts.

4. Pour mixture into a greased and floured 8-inch cake tin.

5. Bake at 325° for about one hour.

6. Decorate top with honey glaze and whole walnuts.

The Children's Own Christmas Cake

For Festive Occasions.

1½ cups mixed fruit (raisins, currants, dates, figs, citron peel, cherries)
½ cup brown sugar
½ cup butter or margarine
½ cup water
1 egg
¼ cup grated carrot
2 cups wholewheat flour
1 tsp. baking powder

1. Place fruit, sugar, margarine or butter, in pan with water. Simmer slowly for 20 mins.

2. Allow to cool, then add beaten egg and stir in flour.

3. Pour into greased 8-inch cake tin.

4. Bake in moderate oven at 300° to 325° for 1½ hours.

Gingerbread

2 cups wholewheat flour
1 tsp. baking powder
pinch of salt
2 tsp. ground ginger
¼ cup raisins
¼ cup margarine
¼ cup brown sugar
½ cup molasses, or ¼ cup
   maple syrup and ¼ cup
   molasses
1 egg with enough milk to make
   up to ½ cup.

1. Mix flour, baking powder, salt, ginger, and raisins in a bowl.

2. Melt margarine, sugar, and molasses in a pan. Add to the flour mixture with beaten egg nd milk.

3. Mix all together well, but do not beat.

4. Pour into greased 8-inch square tin.

5. Bake in moderate oven at 325° for about 45 minutes.

6. When cold, cut into fingers or squares.

This recipe can be adapted to cup cakes. Fill cup cakes 2/3 full. And bake 30 minutes instead.

Yield: 12 cupcakes.

Cookies

Favourite Peanut Butter Cookies

½ cup margarine
½ cup peanut butter
½ cup honey
½ cup brown sugar
1 egg
1¼ cups stone ground
   wholewheat flour
½ tsp. baking powder
¾ tsp. soda
¼ tsp. salt

1. Mix together the margarine, peanut butter, sugar, honey, and egg.

2. Stir in all dry ingredients.

3. Chill dough.

4. Roll into walnut-size balls.

. Place apart on lightly greased baking sheet.

6. Flatten with fork dipped in flour.

7. Bake for 10 to 15 minutes at 375° until set, but not hard.

Yield: About 3 dozen cookies.

Almond Cookies #1

2 cups ground almonds
½ cup brown sugar
barely ½ cup melted butter

1. Add sugar to almonds, and add only enough butter to hold them together.

2. Place on waxed paper and pat into a very thin layer.

3. Cut into small rounds with cookie cutter or upturned glass.

4. Place on cookie sheet and bake at 350° for approx. 12 minutes until lightly browned.

Yield: About 4 dozen cookies.

Great for special parties.

Almond Cookies #2

1½ cups wholewheat flour
1 tsp. baking powder
¼ cup brown sugar
¼ cup ground almonds
2/3 cup margarine
blanched almonds

1. Mix together thoroughly the flour, salt, sugar, and ground almonds.

2. Rub in margarine.

3. Knead well.

4. Roll out to about ¼-inch thickness, and cut into rounds.

5. Place half a blanched almond on the centre of each cookie.

6. Bake on a greased baking sheet at 350° for 15 minutes.

Yield: 2 doz. cookies.

Special Lemon Oatmeal Cookies

½ cup margarine
½ cup honey
½ cup brown sugar
1 egg
1½ tsp. grated lemon rind
1½ tbsp. molasses
½ tsp. vanilla
7/8 cup stone ground wholewheat flour
½ tsp. soda
½ tsp. salt
1½ cups rolled oats

1. Mix together thoroughly the margarine, sugar, egg, lemon rind, molasses, and vanilla.

2. Stir in flour, soda, and salt.

3. Add rolled oats and mix with hands.

4. Press dough into long smooth roll about 3 inches across. Wrap in waxed paper and chill for several hours.

5. Slice into 1/8 inch thick pieces with a sharp knife. Place apart on baking sheet.

6. Bake at 400° for about 8 to 10 minutes till lightly browned.

Yield: About 4 dozen cookies.

Cheese Straws

1 cup wholewheat flour
pinch salt and mustard, if desired
2 tbsp. margarine
½ cup grated mild cheddar cheese
1 egg

Ideal with soups

1. Sift together flour, salt. Rub in margarine.

2. Mix in cheese and egg to make a stiff paste.

3. Roll out very thin. Cut into fingers and place on a greased cookie sheet.

4. Bake at 350° for 15 to 20 minutes.

Nutty Flapjacks

1 tsp. honey
½ cup brown sugar
¼ cup rolled oats
1 cup wholewheat flour
½ cup granola crunch.

1. Melt the margarine and honey.

2. Mix together sugar, oats, flour, and granola crunch.

3. Pour the margarine mixture onto the dry ingredients. Mix thoroughly.

4. Spread dough on a well-greased shallow tin.

5. Bake at 375° for 15 or 20 minutes, just until firm.

6. Cut into fingers while still hot. Leave in tray to cool.

Crunchies

¼ cup margarine
¼ cup vegetable oil or butter
¼ cup brown sugar
1 tbsp. honey
3 tsp. boiling water
few drops of vanilla essence
1 cup wholewheat flour
¼ cup rolled oats

1. Cream together margarine, vegetable oil or butter, and sugar.

2. Add honey and boiling water.

3. Stir in flour and oats and mix well.

4. Roll mixture into walnut size balls and place on greased baking sheet.

5. Bake at 325° for 15 to 20 minutes.

Yield: 3 dozen.

Old-Fashioned Ginger Snaps

2 cups wholewheat flour
1 tsp. baking powder
pinch salt
1 tsp. ground ginger
½ cup brown sugar
½ cup margarine
½ cup honey
1 egg, beaten
1 tbsp. molasses

1. Mix all dry ingredients thoroughly.

2. Warm the margarine, molasses, and honey. Mix together well.

3. To the margarine, molasses and honey mixture, add the dry ingredients and beaten egg alternately, a little at a time.

4. Mix well.

5. Place single teaspoonfuls on a greased baking sheet.

6. Bake at 325° for about 15 minutes.

Yield: 3 dozen.

Refrigerator Cookies

1 cup margarine or butter
1½ cups brown sugar
2 eggs
1 cup wheat germ
1 tsp. vanilla
1 cup wholewheat flour
1 cup soya flour
½ cup non-instant powdered milk
½ cup milk
2 tsp. baking powder
½ tsp. salt

1. Cream together the margarine and sugar.

2. Add the eggs, wheat germ, milk, and vanilla. Mix well.

3. Add all other dry ingredients. Stir only enough to mix well.

4. Turn out onto a floured board and form a roll. Cut roll into ¼ inch slices and place on a baking sheet covered with foil.

5. Bake at 375° for 10 minutes.

6. When cool, remove cookies from foil.

If you wish, the roll of dough can be wrapped in waxed paper and stored in the refrigerator until needed.

Variations

Add any of the following to the above recipe: 1 cup cashew nuts, pecans, walnuts, almonds, peanuts, raisins, currants, chopped dates, figs, or coconut meal.

Pies

Flaky Pie Crust

Basic Pie Crust Recipe

1½ cups wholewheat flour
1 tsp. salt
½ cup wheat germ
½ cup margarine, butter or
   natural lard
¼ cup ice water

1. Sift together the flour and salt.

2. Add wheat germ and stir well.

3. Cut margarine, butter, or lard into the dry ingredients with two knives or pastry blender. Pieces should be about the size of large peas. Do not rub with hands.

4. Add ice water. Mix only enough to moisten ingredients.

5. Turn dough onto floured board. Knead just enough to hold dough together.

6. If crust is to be baked without filling, divide into two equal parts. For a two-crust pie, use a slightly larger amount on the bottom crust.

7. Pat dough quickly into a flat round "ball."

8. Dust top lightly with flour and roll 1/8 inch thick. Use a circular

motion with the rolling pin to shape dough into a perfect circle.

9. Turn pie tin over dough. Slide hand udner dough and invert into pan.

10. Press dough into shape. Trim and flute edges. Make fork perforations at ½ inch intervals on the bottom of the crust.

11. Bake single crusts in a preheated oven at 425° for 8 to 10 minutes. Watch carefully as wheat germ burns easily at high temperatures.

If time permits, it is a good idea to chill dough before using.

Yield: 2 single 9-inch pie shells or 1 double crust.

Crisp Pie Crust

Basic Pie Crust #2

2 cups wholewheat flour
1 tsp. salt
½ cup vegetable oil
¼ cup ice water

1. Sift together the flour and salt.

2. Combine the oil and water and beat with a fork. Pour over flour.

3. Cut liquid into flour with fork.

4. Form into a ball, and proceed as for Flaky Pie Crust.

Yield: 2 single 9-inch pie shells or 1 double crust

Custard Pie

1/3 to ½ cup brown sugar
¼ cup powdered non-instant dry milk
2 cups fresh milk
3 eggs
1 tsp. vanilla
pinch of salt

1. Prepare a 9-inch Flaky Crust as per basic recipe.

2. While crust is baking, combine all ingredients except 1½ cups fresh milk.

3. Beat until smooth, then add 1½ cups fresh milk.

4. Remove pie shell from oven and slip onto serving plate.

5. Grease the same pan generously and pour custard mixture into it.

6. Lower oven temperature to 325° and cook custard mixture for 25 to 30 minutes. (Cooking continues as custard cools.)

7. Immediately before serving, loosen custard with spatula and slip carefully into crust. It is important that this be done just before the pie is to be eaten as the crust will become soggy 30 minutes after the custard is put into it.

Apple Custard Pie

Instead of 2 cups milk, use 1 cup thick applesauce and 1 cup milk. Add grated rind of lemon. This is great.

Banana Custard Pie

Omit vanilla. Add ½ tsp. lemon extract or 1 tsp. grated lemon rind. Immediately before serving, slice 2 bananas into the crust. Slip custard over bananas.

Coconut Pie

Add ½ cup shredded coconut to filling.

Date Nut Pie

Just before pouring into crust, add ½ cup chopped dates and walnuts or pecans to custard mixture.

Rich Curd Tart

Filling

1 cup cottage cheese or
   curds if available
¼ cup brown sugar
¼ cup currants
1 egg
2 tbsp. margarine
pinch cinnamon
pinch nutmeg

1. Line either pie tin or muffin tins with Crisp Pie Crust recipe

2. Melt margarine.

3. Mix in all other ingredients and fill pie tin or muffin tins.

4. Bake in hot oven at 425° for 15 to 20 minutes.

Old Fashioned Treacle Tart

Filling

½ cup golden treacle
1 tbsp. honey
1 tbsp. wholewheat breadcrumbs
1 tsp. lemon juice

1. Line pie pan with Crisp Pie Crust.

2. Warm syrup and honey in pan with breadcrumbs and lemon juice.

3. Pour mixture onto pastry shell.

4. Bake in moderate 375° oven about 30 minutes.

5. If desired, decorate top with pastry trimmings.

Puddings, Desserts and Candies

There was a time when desserts and pudding were a contributing factor toward the meal and not just an extra addition by way of a treat. Desserts can be a good source of nutrition and the aware mother will realise this. You can give your hcild vitamins and even protein in desserts. They need not be just a sticky sugar and flour concoction. All children have a sweet tooth and it is very hard to resist the temptation to give them nothing but empty caloric sweetmeats. But if you start at an early age to accustom them to want and even demand good wholesome sweets this will save a lot of cavities.

There are all sorts of combinations to be had for the asking. Most children like dried fruit, and ground up with nuts and rolled in coconut it can become one of their favourite snacks for school or at home. And if you don't have any time for making desserts or sweetmeats, a large bowl of fruit and nuts on the table after every meal is a great source of nourishment.

Puddings

Yorkshire Pudding

½ cup wholewheat flour
¼ tsp. salt
1 egg
1 cup milk or milk and water

1. Mix all ingredients together and beat gently till smooth and creamy.

2. Oil and heat a shallow tin or 6 muffin cups.

3. Pour batter into tins and bake at 425° to 450° for 20 minutes.

Pudding to be good should be high and crisp. Serve with Nut Mince gravy.

Old Fashioned Rice Pudding

½ cup brown rice, uncooked
1½ cups milk
½ cup cream
½ cup raisins or pitted prunes
1 egg
1 tbsp. honey
cinnamon or nutmeg
1 tbsp. butter

1. Put rice into casserole.

2. Beat egg lightly with milk and cream and pour over rice.

3. Add honey and raisins or prunes.

4. Put knot of butter on top and sprinkle with nutmeg or cinnamon.

5. Bake in a very slow oven at 275° to 300° for 1½ hours.

Countess Pudding

2/3 cup wholewheat flour
1 tsp. baking powder
1/3 cup margarine
1/3 cup brown sugar
2 tbsp. currants
1 tbsp. lemon juice
1 egg
a little milk
¼ cup wheat germ

1. Cream margarine and sugar.

2. Gradually fold in flour and wheat germ alternately with beaten egg and milk.

3. Add currants and lemon juice.

4. Place in greased dish.

5. Bake in moderate oven at 325° for 30 minutes.

Very good served with custard sauce or milk.

Steamed Sponge Pudding

¼ cup margarine
¼ cup brown sugar
1 tsp. baking powder
1 cup unbleached flour
1 egg
1 tbsp. milk

1. Cream margarine and sugar.

2. Gently add flour and baking powder alternately with beaten egg and milk.

3. Place mixture in greased pudding mold. Cover securely with waxed paper.

4. Place in steamer on top of double boiler and steam for 1½ hours.

5. Serve with a custard sauce.

A very good idea for small children is to make this basic recipe and fill 4 to 6 custard cups. After cooking they can be frozen and then reheated within 30 minutes when needed.

Fruit Sponge

Add ¼ cup dried fruit to basic recipe above before pouring into mold.

Ginger Pudding

1 cup wholewheat flour
½ tsp. baking powder
pinch salt
½ tsp. ground ginger
1 tbsp. margarine
1 tbsp. brown sugar
1 tbsp. honey
1 egg

1. Mix together the flour, salt, ginger, and rub in the margarine.

2. Add the other ingredients and mix well.

3. Place mixture in greased pudding mold.

4. Steam for 1½ hours on top of the stove.

5. Serve with custard sauce.

Fruit Crumble

1 cup wholewheat flour
½ tsp. baking powder
¼ cup butter or margarine
¼ cup brown sugar
fruits for filling: chopped apples, apricots, peaches, etc.

1. Place fruit in greased ovenware dish.

2. Rub fat into flour until mixture resembles breadcrumbs.

3. Add sugar and mix thoroughly with a knife and spread over fruit.

4. Smooth over surface. Bake in 350° oven for 30 minutes until top is golden.

Baked Custard

¼ cup brown sugar
½ cup non instant powdered milk
pinch salt
3 whole eggs
½ cup fresh milk
1 tsp. vanilla
1½ cups milk

1. Combine and beat the first six ingredients.

2. When the mixture is smooth, add 1½ cups fresh milk.

3. Pour into shallow, greased baking dish or custard cups and sprinkle with nutmeg.

4. Bake at 300° for about 40 minutes.

Brown Betty

1 cup wheat germ
2 tsp. cinnamon
½ cup brown sugar
2 tbsp. butter
¼ cup honey
3 to 5 tart cooking apples, peeled and sliced

1. Mix thoroughly the wheat germ, cinnamon, sugar, and butter.

2. Sprinkle half the above mixture over the bottom of a greased 8- or 9-inch pan.

3. Add ¼ cup honey to the apples.

4. Put apples over wheat germ mixture and sprinkle remainder on top.

5. Bake at 375° for 30 minutes. Do not overbake.

6. Serve with cream or milk.

Date Ice Cream

Soak ½ cup dates in 1 cup milk several hours or overnight. Place in blender and add:
1 cup cream
1 tsp. vanilla
dash of salt

1. Cover and run machine until thoroughly blended.

2. Put into freezing tray and freeze.

3. For smoother dessert remove once and blend or beat smooth.

4. Return to tray and finish freezing.

Strawberry Mousse

1 pint heavy cream
1 pint strawberries hulled and
  washed
¼ cup honey
1 sprig mint

1. Whip cream in blender or with beater until stiff.

2. Turn into bowl.

3. Reserve six large strawberries as garnish.

4. Blend remaining strawberries, honey, and mint till smooth.

5. Fold gently into the whipping cream.

6. Freeze without stirring in ice tray of refrigerator. Serve with whole strawberries.

Lemon Ice Cream

(in blender)

juice and rind of 2 lemons
½ cup non-instant powdered
  milk
1 cup milk
4 tbsp. honey
pinch of salt
1 tsp. Powdered Fruit Rind as
  below

1. Whip cream in blender.
2. Turn into bowl.

3. Blend all other ingredients until smooth, and fold into cream.

4. Freeze until firm in ice tray of refrigerator.

5. Beat twice while the ice cream is freezing.

Powdered Fruit Rind

1. Select orange, lemon or grapefruit rinds which have not been artificially sprayed or coloured.

2. Wash and dry rinds.

3. Place on cooky sheets in warm place to dry.

4. When thoroughly dry, pulverize in the blender.

5. Store in tight screw-top jars. Use in breads, muffins, ice cream, desserts, cookies, beverages, confections, and spreads.

Blender Berry Ice Cream

¾ cup heavy cream
3 cups fresh berries
3 tbsp. honey
½ cup fruit juice
juice of 1 lemon
1 sprig mint

1. Whip cream in blender.

2. Turn into bowl.

3. Blend rest of ingredients until smooth, and fold into cream. Freeze in ice trays of refrigerator until firm, beating twice while the ice cream is freezing.

Honey Ice Cream

(uncooked)

2 eggs, separated
½ cup heavy cream, whipped
1 tsp. vanilla
3 heaping tbsp of honey

1. Beat yolks till thick.

2. Add honey gradually.

3. Blend in cream and vanilla.

4. Freeze until almost firm.

5. Place in chilled bowl.
6. Fold in stiffly beaten egg whites.

7. Beat all until smooth.

8. Put into ice tray of refrigerator.

9. Freeze again till firm.

Apple Lemon Snow

1 cup applesauce
2 egg whites
1 tbsp. honey
1 tbsp. grated lemon rind

1. Place all ingredients in deep bowl and beat with an egg beater until white and as thick as whipped cream.

2. Serve piled into sherbet glasses.

3. Top with finely ground nuts.

Banana Apricot Sherbert

2 cups of apricot puree or fresh apricots
2 bananas
1 cup orange juice
½ cup cream or yoghurt
honey to taste

1. Place all ingredients in a blender and run until smooth.

2. Pour into ice cube trays or one large tray.

3. Freeze until hard at about ¼ inch round the edges.

4. Scrape into large bowl and beat until smooth and fluffy.

5. Refreeze.

Makes 1 quart of sherbet.

Variations

Use peaches in place of apricots, and apple juice instead of orange. Yoghurt gives a tart taste while cream makes a richer product.

High Protein Ice Cream

4 eggs
1 cup milk
1 banana (or 1 cup of berries in
  season)
1 tsp. vanilla
2 tbsp. honey
1/3 cup protein supplement
  (optional)
¼ cup safflower oil
2 cups heavy cream

1. Blend eggs, milk, and fruit for 2 minutes; or beat eggs well with a rotary beater, then add the milk and fruit.

2. Add the vanilla, honey, supplement, safflower oil, and beat well.

3. Add heavy cream. Mix well.

4. Pour into 2 deep freezer trays and freeze.

5. Stir once during freezing or beat well for really fluffy smooth ice cream.

This makes 10 to 12 servings but will not last long.

Rice Cakes

2 eggs
1¾ cup cooked brown rice
3 tbsp. wheat germ
¼ tsp. sea salt

1. Beat eggs slightly.

2. Add rice, wheat germ, and salt.

3. Heat griddle to medium heat (325°).

4. Add 1 tbsp. butter.

5. Drop batter by tablespoons onto griddle.

6. Flatten with back of spoon so cakes will be thin.

7. When crisp and golden (about 4 minutes), turn cakes over and cook other side.

8. Serve with honey or maple syrup.

Spicy Peanut Butter Pudding

½ cup soft butter
½ cup unpasturized peanut butter
2 eggs, beaten
1/3 cup honey
grated rind and juice of whole lemon
¾ cup wholewheat flour
¼ cup soya four or wheat germ
pinch of salt
¼ tsp. each of nutmeg and allspice
1/8 tsp. baking powder
1 cup chopped dates or raisins
1 cup raw shredded carrots
1 cup chopped nuts
½ cup crushed drained pineapple

1. Cream butter, and blend in peanut butter.

2. Beat in the eggs, honey, lemon rind, and juice.

3. Add the sifted dry ingredients and beat well.

4. Stir in the dates or raisins, carrots, nuts, and pineapple.

5. Pack into well-oiled custard cups (5-6 oz.) and set in pan of hot water.

6. Bake at 350° for 55 to 60 minutes.

7. Unmold from dishes and serve warm with cream or whipped cream for a special occasion.

Apple Date Butter

1 large apple, peeled, cored
  and quartered
½ cup apple juice or pineapple
  juice
12 large dates, pitted

1. Blend together the apple and the juice.

2. Begin adding dates, 3 or 4 at a time.

3. Cover and blend.

4. Keep adding dates till mixture is smooth and as thick as you wish.

5. Good on wholewheat bread, banana loaf, or apple slices.

Makes about 1½ lbs. of apple date butter.

Dessert Sauces

Blender Almond Sauce

1 cup almonds
½ tbsp. orange rind
¼ cup honey
1 tbsp. oil
1 cup wheat germ
¼ cup sweet cider or apple
  juice

1. Grind almonds in blender.

2. Add rest of ingredients.

3. Blend until smooth.

4. Serve on puddings or ice cream.

Fruited Honey Sauce

3 pears or apples, peeled,
　cored, and finely diced.
1 cup honey
1 tsp. lemon juice
1 tsp. butter
¼ tsp. cinnamon

1. Combine all ingredients in a small saucepan.

2. Cook slowly, stirring often, until fruit is tender.

Can be served hot or cold.

Yield: About two cups.

Honey Coconut Sauce

¾ cup honey
2 tbsp. melted butter
¾ cup unsweetened shredded
　coconut, toasted*

Combine all ingredients and use on desserts.

*To toast, spread shredded coconut on a baking sheet in a 350° oven and stir often for 5 to 7 minutes.

Nut Butters

Nuts are such an excellent source of protein, the B vitamins, unsaturated fatty acids, that they should be used much more than they are in the average home. Nut butters make a delicious change from jams and jellies, and are so easy to make yourself. Aside from their contribution to good health, the children love them. Use them on breads and fruit.

Nut butters should be made in a nut grinder but the fine mill on your blender will work very well. Make them in quite small quantities and refrigerate. They should be made from fresh unsalted nuts. They can be thinned with milk and used as toppings on cereals or desserts.

Use a cupful of nuts at a time and grind to the consistency of flour. Peanuts will need a little extra oil. Almonds, cashews, walnuts, and filberts have enough oil of their own and will very quickly become buttery.

Nut Butter Spread

1 cup nuts
½ cup sunflower seeds, hulled
½ cup sesame seeds
oil
honey to taste

1. Grind nuts and seeds.

2. Blend in enough oil to make mixture into thick paste.

3. Add honey to taste.

4. Blend thoroughly.

5. Pack into container.

6. Refrigerate.

Combination nut butter spreads

Try nut butter of your choice with lemon juice and raisins. Try nut butter of your choice with chopped green peppers and celery. Find your own favourite combination.

Candies

Children will always be children and will want sweetmeats, and indeed why not. But there are ways of adding nutrition even to candies and staying in control of the sugar content.

Date Nut Balls

(uncooked)

1 cup dates
¼ cup raisins
1 cup pecans or almonds
  or filberts

1. Put all ingredients through food grinder or blender.

2. Form into small balls.

3. Roll in grated coconut.

Makes 2 dozen balls.

Peanut Butter Goody

(uncooked)

¼ cup blackstrap molasses
¼ cup honey
½ cup peanut butter
1 cup non-instant powdered
  milk
¼ cup raisins
¼ cup chopped nuts (optional)
¼ cup Carob powder

1. Mix everything in a roomy bowl and form a ball with it.

2. Add more powdered milk if necessary.

3. Knead on a board till stiff.

4. Cut into small squares and roll in carob powder. After an hour if the children can wait, it's ready.

Apricot Sweetmeat

(uncooked)

1 cup dried apricots (without sulphur dioxide if possible)
½ cup sunflower seeds
6 dates, pitted

1. Grind nuts and seeds.

2. Form into small logs.

3. Roll in chopped nuts.

4. You may make into one large roll if desired and cut with sharp knife when required.

Sesame Brittle

2 cups raw sugar
2 cups sesame seeds
1 tsp. vanilla or lemon extract

1. Place the sugar in a heavy pan and heat gradually, stirring all the while until sugar melts and forms a golden syrup. Take care not to burn the sugar.

2. Remove from heat and stir in seeds and vanilla.

3. Pour onto buttered cookie sheets to make a thin layer.

4. Cool.

5. When cool, break into pieces.

Yield: About one pound.

Sesame Seed Candies

1 cup sesame seeds
honey to taste
¼ tsp. almond or lemon extract
½ cup raisins
18 walnut halves, approx.

1. Place the seeds in blender, and blend until they are a smooth mass.

2. Turn onto a board and knead in the honey.

3. Knead in the extract.

4. Work in the raisins and make the mixture into a compact ball.

5. Pinch off pieces and press half a walnut onto the top. Store in covered container in the refrigerator.

Peanut Butter Delights

½ cup peanut butter
2 cups shredded coconut
4 tbsp. fresh lemon juice
1 tbsp. brewers yeast
¼ cup honey

1. Mix all ingredients together.

2. Spread into oiled square pan.

3. Chill, and then cut into squares.

4. Wrap in wax paper.

Great for the lunch box.

Poppy Seed Candy

Absolutely different and delicious.

½ lb. poppy seeds
¼ cup raw brown sugar
1 cup honey
1 cup chopped nuts
(pecans and almonds are
particularly good)

1. Let poppy seeds soak overnight in boiling water. Next morning, drain.

2. Pound seeds with pestle or put through food blender.

3. Cook sugar and honey over low heat till sugar dissolves.

4. Add poppy seeds and cook until thick, stirring often (30 to 40 minutes).

5. Test by dropping onto board. If it holds it shape, it's ready for the next step.

6. Stir in nuts, and cook one more minute.

7. Turn onto wet board. Let cool for 5 to 10 minutes.

8. Cut into 1-inch squares with sharp knife dipped into cold water.

Iced Banana

1 banana
1 spoonful grated coconut

1. Peel banana and enclose in foil.

2. Put in freezer compartment for a few hours.

3. Serve rolled in coconut and sliced; or put it on a stick and it's a popsicle.

Frozen banana has the same texture as ice cream and children love it. Surely the easiest of "candies" to make and also doubles as a dessert.

Carrot Candy

(which is really a type of Halvah, would you believe?)

2 cups carrots grated as fine
   as possible
2 quarts milk
2 cups brown sugar
1 cup honey
4 tbsp. melted butter
almonds slivered, or nuts of
   your choice

1. Scald the milk and add the finely grated carrots.

2. Cook over very low heat. The finer the carrot the more delicate will be the texture.

3. Do not scorch. It will take 40 minutes to bring to the right consistency, but it is worth it.

4. At the end of that time, add the honey and sugar and continue to stir till it is dissolved.

5. Then add the melted butter. Stir till it has been absorbed. The candy should be a bright orange colour.

6. Turn out onto ungreased platter and sprinkle nuts on top.

7. Cut into bite-size pieces.

The quantities may seem large, but I find this goes very quickly.

Fruit Lollipops

½ lb. raisins dates mixed
½ lb. dried apricots
1 cup Brazil nuts
1 cup wheat germ
½ cup honey

1. Grind fruit and nuts.

2. Add the rest of the ingredients.

3. Shape into balls and put on skewers.

Makes about 4 dozen lollipops

Coconut Drops

1½ cups of coconut shreds
6 tbsp. honey
1 egg white, beaten stiff
pinch of cinnamon

1. Cook coconut and honey together in top of double boiler for 10 to 15 minutes.

2. When coconut is transparent fold in egg white.

3. Continue to cook, stirring occasionally for 10 to 15 minutes, or until mixture is sticky.

4. Add cinnamon.

5. Drop by teaspoonfuls on lightly oiled cookie sheet.

6. Bake at 325° for 20 minutes.

7. When done, remove from sheet at once.

Granola Crunch Candy

honey
shredded unsweetened coconut
Crunchy Granola

1. Add enough honey and coconut to the Granola to make it stick together.

2. Form into balls.

3. Wrap in waxed paper.

Good for the lunch box.

Carob Fudge

2 cups raw sugar
6 tbsp. Carob powder
2 tbsp. butter
2/3 cup milk
pinch of salt
1½ tsp. vanilla

1. Combine the sugar, Carob powder, butter, milk, and salt in a heavy saucepan.

2. Heat, stirring until sugar is dissolved.

3. Continue to boil without stirring until candy thermometer registers 225° or a drop placed in a bowl of cold water forms a soft ball.

4. Add vanilla.

5. Cool to lukewarm.

6. Beat until creamy.

7. Pour into buttered pan and cool, then cut into squares.

Basic Quick Frosting

2 egg whites
¾ cup raw sugar pulverized
  in the blender
1 tbsp. fresh lemon juice
  or ½ teaspoon cream of tartar

1. Have ingredients in rounded refrigerator bowl.

2. Beat at fast speed till very stiff.

3. Clean off beaters, cover the bowl and keep in refrigerator until needed. Lasts well in covered container.

Variations

Apple Frosting: Add 1 apple cut in thin slices to frosting. Add cinamon if desired.

Banana Frosting: Add 1 sliced banana to frosting.

Carob Frosting: Beat 2 tbsp. carob and 1 tsp. vanilla with other frosting ingredients.

Sesame Frosting: Add 1/3 cup sesame seed to finished frosting.

Carob Walnut Frosting

1½ cups heavy cream
2 tbsp. raw sugar pulverized
2 tbsp. Carob powder
1 tsp. vanilla
½ cup walnuts

1. Whip the cream till very thick.

2. Then add the other ingredients gently, and keep beating until they are blended.

3. Spread on cake and top with sunflower seeds and walnuts.

4. Store in refrigerator.

Makes about 3 cups

Seafoam Frosting

2 egg whites
1 cup raw sugar, pulverized
   in blender
1 tsp. vanilla
¼ cup cold water

1. Put all ingredients but vanilla in the top of a double boiler and keep over boiling water, beating constantly, for 7 minutes or until mixture holds peaks.

2. Remove from heat, add vanilla, and beat until thick

3. Spread between layers of cake, and on top and sides.

Will stay soft if refrigerated.

Peanut Butter Frosting

2 tbsp. butter
¾ cup smooth peanut butter
1 tsp. vanilla
1 cup raw sugar pulverized
   in the blender
½ cup light cream
¼ cup honey
chopped peanuts (optional)

1. With mixer at low speed, blend butter, peanut butter, carob and vanilla.

2. Add sugar alternately with cream until mixture can be spread.

3. Stir in honey.

4. Sprinkle with chopped peanuts.

Makes about 3 cups.

Jams and Preserves

For those of you who really feel ambitious and enjoy cooking, I have included a few recipes for making jam and preserving. I use honey or brown sugar instead of white sugar and have not as yet had to use any commercial pectins. The only difference is that I probably have to boil my jams and marmalades a little longer, but they have always worked out so well and the family enjoy them so much that I don't mind the extra time. Children love to have a spread for their toasts and bread and butter, and nothing is quite as good as honey, and mother's homemade jams.

Honey Peach Jam

¾ tsp. allspice
3 tsp. stick cinnamon
1½ tsp. whole cloves
3 pounds peaches, pureed
2 cups honey
3 tbsp. fresh lemon juice
¾ cup orange juice, unsweetened and fresh if possible

1. Put spices in cheesecloth.

2. Cook all ingredients until mixture thickens.

3. Remove spices.

4. Pour jam into hot sterilized jars.

5. Seal with paraffin and cover.

Makes 3 pints.

Blender Apple Jam

5 cups blender-made apple
  puree*

1 tsp. allspice

1½ tsp. cinnamon

¼ cup lemon juice

7½ cups raw sugar pulverized,
  or 8 cups honey

½ cup homemade pectin (see
  page 156)

1. Into a saucepan put all the
above ingredients, except the
pectin

2. Boil for 1 minute on high heat
stirring constantly.

3. Remove from heat.

4. At once stir in the homemade
pectin.

5. Skim off any foam with a
wooden spoon.

6. Then stirr for 5 minutes to
prevent floating fruit.

*Makes about 6 one-pound jars or
12 medium glassfuls.*

7. Ladle into jars and seal.

*Apple Puree

1. Peel 5 pounds of apples and
cut into eighths and core.

2. Fill blender container half full
of apple slices and add ½ cup
water.

3. Cover and blend on high
speed for 15 seconds.

4. Continue blending more fruit
and water until all the fruit has
been blended.

Carrot Rhubarb Jam

3 cups raw carrots, grated
6 cups rhubarb, diced
juice and grated rind of
   3 oranges
1 cup honey
½ tsp. salt
¼ tsp. nutmeg

1. Pour some boiling water over rhubarb. (This reduces any objectionable oxalic acid.) Let stand for 10 minutes.

2. Drain.

3. Mix all ingredients and let stand overnight.

4. Next morning, bring to a slow boil.

5. Cook only until rhubarb is transparent and mixture is thickened.

6. Pour into hot sterilized jars.

Makes 2½ pints.

7. Seal.

Honey Apple Butter

2 quarts of tart cooking apples
   with skins
1 tsp. cinnamon
¼ tsp. allspice
½ tsp. mace
2 cups honey
juice and grated rind of
   ½ lemon
2 cups mint vinegar or pure
   apple cider vinegar

1. Core and slice apples.

2. Put with all other ingredients into large kettle.

3. Cook slowly for several hours stirring frequently till thick.

4. Pour into hot sterilized jars.

5. Seal.

Makes 6 pints.

Quick Orange Marmalade.

1 cup honey
2 whole oranges, cut in pieces
rinds of 4 oranges

Blend all together well.

Makes 1½ pints of marmalade.

Serve on hot pancakes or use to top ice cream.

Variation
Add ¼ cup fresh mint leaves before blending.

Chunky Orange Marmalade

5 lbs. whole fruit (1 grapefruit
   can be included for flavour)
juice of 3 fresh lemons
5 lbs. raw sugar or honey
2 quarts water

1. Wash fruit well and place whole in jam kettle with water.

2. Boil slowly for 3 to 4 hours until fruit is tender.

3. Take fruit and cut up with sharp knife and fork, taking care to save all the pips and juice.

4. Place the pips in a piece of cheesecloth to be hung over the side of the jam kettle or pot.

5. When cut to your satisfaction, place all the fruit and juice back in the pan and add sugar.

6. Bring to full rolling boil and continue to boil until at setting stage, approx. 1 hour.

7. Add lemon juice after 30 minutes.

8. Take bag of pips out when set.

9. Test on saucer which has been in the freezer. It will jell when ready.

10. Cool, and skim off any excess foam.

11. Ladle into bottles or jars and seal with paraffin. If not sealed while hot wait until completely cooled to seal.

Chunky marmalade liked by the whole family.

Homemade Pectin

Use firm ripe apples.

1. Wash apples.

2. Cut into thin slices.

3. Add 1 pint of water for each pound of fruit used.

4. Boil slowly in covered kettle for 15 minutes.

5. Strain off free running juice through 1 thickness of cheese-cloth.

6. Return pulp to kettle.

7. Add small amount of water again.

8. Cook slowly for 15 minutes.

9. Let stand 10 minutes longer.

10. Strain through 1 thickness of cheesecloth.

11. Squeeze out all the juice. Combine the two juices.

12. There should be about 1 quart for each pound of apples used.

This stock may be used immediately for blending with other fruit juices to make jelly or it may be preserved for later use.

To preserve: Heat stock to boiling point. Pour immediately into hot sterilized jars. Seal. Invert jars to cool.

Parties and Festive Occasions

Parties for young children do not have to be a necessary evil. They can be fun. If you keep a few simple rules in mind, you can't go wrong. Remember that a "party" to a small child is a few friends plus their favourite sandwiches. Don't wear yourself out trying to impress them and their parents with complicated cooking. Children love the old familiar things; and contrary to popular opinion, they don't always go for gooey sticky cakes. I have found that children at ages 3, 4, 5, and 6 never eat much at parties. The ravenous "stuffing" probably happens a little later, around 9 and 10.

I once heard someone say, and I tend to agree, that the golden rule for a youngster's party is to invite as many guests as there are candles on the birthday cake and keep the party short. If you child has a zillion friends, you can solve the problem by having some of them over another day. By all means, don't try to be formal or "proper." Many a "proper" mother has ruined her child's birthday party. Box lunch type meals are fun; and on a good day, nothing could be more fun than a picnic in the back yard. On a cold or rainy day, a picnic on the floor delights children.

When should we start giving parties? Well, a good rule of thumb is: Don't, for the one- and two-year-old. (A "party" with only the family is enough.) However, if you feel you must, keep it brief and limit it to one to three children. After all, when you child is that young, the "party" is really for you and not the child. I must confess that for my child's first birthday, I was so bursting with motherly pride that I did have a few friends and their children to tea, and really, it was not much fun. Children really begin to enjoy social occasions at the age of three, and a party can be very enjoyable for them and you. If you play games, keep them as simple as possible — and have the games before tea or lunch. It is fun to listen to records and "dance" too. Always have plenty of toys accessible as it helps the shy children to get acquainted. At the ages of two and three, children still go off and play by themselves, so don't worry if there is a child who won't "join" in. He or she may later; and if not, it is of no great importance.

Preparation for the party usually includes the invitations. Let your child help with them and, perhaps, even attempt to make his own. It is a lot of fun to have balloons blown up and the name, date, and place marked on them with marking pencils. Then let the air out of the balloons and send them in an envelope. Always specify the length of the party on the invitation so that there is no doubt. For me, one and a half hours is just right. One hour for games and fun, and thirty minutes or so for refreshments and the cake. As so many children at 3, 4, and 5 years are still having afternoon naps, it is sometimes very worthwhile to have the party at lunch time and then the little ones can go off for their rest time.

Up until the age of four or so, mothers may wish to stay with their child. In some cases, mothers may prefer to go away and leave the child. However, not all children are alike and for some youngsters, it is a frightening experience if the mother is suddenly not there.

Elaborate "menus" do not work so I have given a few recipes for fillings for sandwiches and cakes and cookies which have always proved popular with us.

Butterscotch Brownies

¼ cup vegetable oil
1 tbsp. molasses
½ cup broken nuts, walnuts or pecans
2 eggs
2 tsp. vanilla
1 cup wheat germ
pinch salt
½ cup non instant dried milk powder
½ tsp. baking powder

1. Combine all ingredients except milk and baking powder.

2. Stir well, and then mix in the milk and baking powder.

3. Spread in 8x8 pan lined with heavy greased paper and bake at 350° for 30 minutes.

4. Be careful not to overbake.

5. Turn out of pan immediately and remove paper.

6. Cut into squares while still hot.

Yield: 16 brownies.

Date Loaf

½ cup brown sugar
1 tbsp. margarine or vegetable oil
1 egg
1½ cups pitted dates
1½ cups boiling water
2¼ cups wholewheat or unbleached white flour
1 tsp. baking powder
½ tsp. baking soda
pinch of salt
1 cup broken walnuts or pecans

1. Pour boiling water over dates and let cool.

2. Mix thoroughly the margarine or oil, sugar, and egg.

3. Then mix in the cooled dates and water.

4. Stir in the dry ingredients, mix well, and last of all add the nuts.

5. Pour into a well-greased 9x5x3 loaf pan.

6. Let stand 20 minutes before baking.

7. Bake until the wooden pick you insert comes out clean. This is approximately 60 to 70 minutes in a 350° oven.

Can be served with butter, but is delicious without. Tastes best when it is made the day before use. Will keep for days in an airtight tin.

Carrot Cake with Nuts

3 cups wholewheat flour
2 tsp. baking powder
1½ tsp. baking soda
2 tsp. cinnamon
1 cup vegetable oil
1½ cups brown sugar
4 whole eggs
2 cups grated carrots
1 cup chopped nuts

1. Sift flour, soda, baking powder, and cinnamon together.

2. Add the rest of the ingredients, mixing well.

3. Bake for one hour and 15 minutes at 300°.

4. Press top with finger. If the cake is done, it will spring back.

You can use a loaf pan or an angel food pan for this cake. It will freeze well, and can be thawed out by wrapping it in foil and putting it into a warm oven for ten minutes. I usually find it a good idea to double the quantity and make two, freeze one for a later date.

Carrot Cake with Raisins

1½ cup grated carrots
1-1/3 cup water
1½ cups brown sugar
1 cup raisins
1 tsp. cinnamon
2 tsp. butter
2 tsp. baking soda
2 cups wholewheat flour
½ tsp. salt

1. Cook carrots, water, sugar and raisins in a saucepan. Boil 7 to 8 minutes.

2. When tender, add butter and cinnamon.

3. Add dry ingredients to mixture.

4. Bake in loaf tin or 9-inch square pan at 375° for 45 minutes.

Also easy to freeze.

Coconut Butter Cake

(With the coconut inside)

1 cup butter
2 cups brown sugar
4 eggs
1 cup milk
1 cup flaked coconut
2½ cups unbleached flour
2 tsp. baking powder
1 tsp. vanilla
¼ cup nuts, (pecans are best, or
  walnuts)

1. Cream butter and add sugar. Beat well.

2. Add eggs.

3. Alternately add sifted dry ingredients with the milk.

4. Add coconut with the vanilla.

5. Grease a 10-inch tube pan and sprinkle nuts on the bottom. Add the batter.

6. Bake 1 to 1½ hours at 350°

7. Cool for a few minutes and turn out.

No need to frost, the crunchy topping is enough.

A Few Tasty Sandwich Fillings

Cheese Date Whizz

½ cup grated cheddar cheese
1 tbsp. honey
½ cup pitted and chopped dates
milk or cream to mix

Blend everything to the required consistency and serve in gaily coloured egg cups. Put plastic knives on the table for the children to make their own sandwiches.

Tuna and Cheese

½ cup mayonnaise (homemade)
½ cup tuna fish flaked or in
  chunks
1 tsp. green onion
¼ cup cream cheese

Blend in blender and serve on bread or as above.

Peanut Crackle

½ cup peanut butter
¼ cup broken nuts
½ cup banana

Blend as above and serve either way.

Cream Cheese and Nut Filling

1 cup soft cream cheese
½ cup broken nuts
½ cup prunes and apricots
  mixed (dried fruit is better for
  this, cooked and pitted)

Blend all ingredients in the blender.

Tomato Egg Filling

½ cup chopped tomatoes, with
  or without skins
2 hardboiled eggs, peeled
½ cup mayonnaise
1 small green onion

Blend in blender and let children serve themselves, or make sandwiches in the usual way.

Additional Things for the Refreshment Tray

curled carrots
celery curls
watermelon sticks
banana slices
cheese in various shapes
apple slices, with skin on
orange slices or segments
any fresh berries in season
cheese sticks and balls
bread sticks
prunes stuffed with cream cheese or nut paste
dates
celery stuffed with peanut butter and cut in inch-long pieces

Always keep the vegetables in a plastic bag in the crisper and put on the table just before serving.

Sweetmeats

Date Coconut Carob Balls

(uncooked)

1 pound dates, pitted and
   chopped
½ cup shredded coconut
2 tbsp. warm water
6 tbsp. Carob powder
1 tbsp. Powdered Fruit Rind

1. Mix all ingredients together.

2. Shape into balls.

3. Roll in additional coconut or powdered sugar.

Wholewheat Oatmeal Chews

2 cups wholewheat flour
1 cup oatmeal flour (if not available, grind 1 cup oatmeal in your blender till fine)
½ cup soy flour
½ tsp. salt
1 cup coconut
½ cup honey
½ cup molasses
1 cup oil
¼ cup powdered Fruit Rind
2 tbsp. nutritional yeast (optional)

1. Sift flours and salt.

2. Add all other ingredients.

3. Blend well with spoon.

4. Drop by teaspoonfuls on oiled cookie sheet.

Bake at 350° for 10 minutes or until brown.

Makes 4 dozen chews.

Festive Colours for Foods

To make your food colouring is really very simple.

For pink:
Grate raw beet and squeeze in square of nylon net.
Squeeze pomegranate seeds as above.

For green:
Chop parsley or spinach very finely. Squeeze through nylon net.

For yellow:
Grate raw carrots and squeeze as above.

For tinting coconut:
Add 1 teaspoon or more of colour desired to each cup of coconut in a glass jar with top. Shake until all is tinted. Place plastic bags over your hands to prevent staining while squeezing.

Home Remedies and General Helps

We live today in an age of convenience, and so we are used to calling our doctor on the phone for even minor accidents. Doctors are a very necessary part of our lives, but for little mishaps some basic knowledge can be a great help to a mother. Home remedies are usually based on common sense and knowing some pertinent facts often keeps panic at bay and helps you solve your own problems with children.

Scrapes and Bumps
For instance, it was not until I had children of my own that I fully realized the untold benefits of *plain old tap water*. There are times when your child seems to be continually falling and scraping his head, elbows and knees. When he comes to you with a rapidly swelling lump, immediately take a cloth and soak it in as cold a water as you can get from the tap and apply it to the bump like a compress. Hold it there and change it frequently in the next few minutes. The swelling will go down rapidly and the chances are there will be no ugly bruise.

Stings
"Mother, something stung me!" How often we hear this cry in the summer. If you have nothing else on hand cold wet earth is good to rub on the affected part. If you can see the sting then you will have more of a problem to remove it. But for those annoying stings from wasps and flies, raw potato, lemon slices, poppy leaves, marigold or nasturtium leaves rubbed onto the spot are very good and will alleviate the pain. I keep an infusion of camomile flowers in a bottle in the summer. This contains a substance which is known to be an antihistamine. Applied before going out in the sun it also acts as a burn preventative, as well as an insect repellent.

Bleeding
Bleeding from a scrape or a cut can be stopped quickly and efficiently by applying a pad of cotton wool or a clean handkerchief dipped in *hot* water and applied firmly to the spot.

A Stomach ache.
Make caraway, anise, fennel, or camomile tea. This will help the gases in the stomach to escape and will lessen the discomfiture.

Diaper Rash
On the small baby this can be prevented by always using from the very beginning good old fashioned corn starch. This is a natural product which also heals, so that it is a good thing to try. For badly chafed bottoms, make a mixture of cornstarch and water in a paste and apply gently with cotton. Don't be afraid to put on quite a bit as it dries rapidly and comes off.

Jambed fingers
Fingers that have been caught in the door usually hurt worse than a cut. Hold the finger in olive oil or any other vegetable oil. Then wrap it in an oil-soaked bandage. The pain will then go away very quickly.

Choking
Choking because of a piece of food which can't be spit out or swallowed can be helped by gently sticking your forefinger down the childs throat, thus forcing everything to be vomited out, along with the offending piece of food.

WARNING

Keep all detergents, bleaches, paints, poison sprays, cleaners, turpentine, drugs, and other medicines out of the baby's or toddler's reach. Most accidents have been proved to happen when the child is in his second or third year. Don't take a chance and leave your baby in the bathroom or the kitchen while you answer the telephone or the door. Take the child with you or be sure to place any dangerous objects far out of reach.

Travel Sickness
Many mothers have found that car sickness or air sickness can be prevented if the child's diet is adequately supplied with Vitamin B-2. Add a tablet of this to juice or beverage before travel. Tablets can be had in 25 milligram sizes. If your child is too young to swallow the tablet, crush it first and add to the drink. If your child has this sort of "sickness" quite regularly it might be a good idea to check his diet and see if he is getting enough of all the B Vitamins. If not, a teaspoon of brewers' yeast can be mixed into juice or sprinkled on cereals daily.

Carrot Juice
While rich in Vitamin A carrot juice is also dreadful for staining on bibs and

shirt fronts of small babies. Immediately rinse in *cold* water, never warm or hot. Then rub with soap.

Grass Stains

On white clothes grass stains can be taken out with butter. Tar stains can be removed in the same way. Rub butter on the soiled part and gently rub off with a soft cloth.

Laxatives

Laxatives should not have to be given to small children and if the diet is adequate in bulk, constipation will not occur. Instead of giving a commercial laxative, try prune juice or whole prunes at first, or fig juice and whole figs. The old adage about "an apple a day keeps the doctor away" has a lot of common sense behind it.

Teeth Cleaning

Young children are not always able to brush their teeth so a natural aid that is beneficial to cleaning the mouth before going to bed is an apple or a drink of pure apple juice or strawberry juice. Apple is preferable.

Baths

Bathtime is a fun time of the day for children. Don't use too much of the so-called water softeners and bubble baths which are on the market today, supposedly for children. In winter months, especially, most homes are so dry and children's skins are so tender, that many of these bubble baths will irritate and chafe the skin.

In the summer months it is better not to bathe at nighttime as you will wash off the beneficial oil formed there by the exposure to the sun's rays, which manufacture Vitamin D. Some authorities say that if a child has a good exposure to sunshine in the summer he will have enough Vitamin D to last all winter, as this is one of the vitamins that the body can store.

Sunbathing

Fresh air and sunshine are very important to a child but don't overdo the sun bathing bit. Children get enough exposure running round in the garden, and should always wear something on their heads during the really hot part of the day to protect their necks and heads. My children enjoy and have everday what we call an "air bath". For 5 minutes or so before they get dressed in the morning they run around without their clothes, letting the skin breath; it gives them a glow all over.

Recommended Books

Let's Have Healthy Children
Let's Cook It Right
Let's Eat Right to Keep Fit   Adele Davis
Let's Get Well

Publisher: New American Library, Inc.

Thank you, Dr. Lamaze   Majorie Karmel

Publisher: J.B. Lippincott Co., New York

The Motherly Art of Breastfeeding   La Leche League

Publisher: La Leche League Interstate Printers and Publishers

New York Times Natural Foods Cookbook   Jean Hewitt

Publisher: Avon Books, Quadrangel Books, Inc., New York

Better Food for Better Babies and their Families   Gena Larson

Publisher: Keats Publishing, Inc., New Cannaan, Connecticut

INDEX

W

Y

Z